WANT LUSTY, LIVELY,

TENDER LOVING CARE?

MEET Vera, an enterprising and warmhearted girl whose unique lay-away plan brought pleasure to hundreds of lonely young patriots and several hundred thousand dollars to her special retirement fund

. . . Lieutenant Carolyn Polaski, the only woman at an isolated radar station, and the "system" she organized

. . . "Dancing Fingers" Margale, the amorous dentist

. . . Ginger Whip, the spectacularly endowed nurse who wrote an official report in collaboration with a pornographic novelist

. . . Clyde Hardman, who sweet-talked a nurse into posing for 1600 groovy feet of nudies—for a government training film;

. . . and dozens and dozens more.

Tender Loving Care

The Uninhibited Memoirs
of Two Air Force Nurses

Joni Moura
and Jackie Sutherland

Illustrated by Bill Wenzel

A FAWCETT CREST BOOK
Fawcett Publications, Inc., Greenwich, Conn.

TENDER LOVING CARE

THIS BOOK CONTAINS THE COMPLETE TEXT OF THE
ORIGINAL HARDCOVER EDITION.

A Fawcett Crest Book reprinted by arrangement with
Bartholomew House Ltd.

Library of Congress Catalog Card Number: 71-79432

Published by Fawcett World Library
67 West 44th Street, New York, N.Y. 10036
Printed in the United States of America

Contents

To
DONALD BAIN

Chapter 1

"Uncle Sam Wants Us?"

It all started with Veronica Lake. At least it did for me. I'm an only child, and that meant I had no one to fight off in matters of choosing which television show to watch. This was especially true late at night. My parents retired early, and I was left with an open kitchen and freedom of viewing choice.

That particular night, securely wrapped in my terrycloth robe and sated with a large glass of chocolate cream soda and bag of home-popped popcorn, I sat transfixed as the television screen flickered its cold blue light into the darkness of our living room. Unknown to the sleepy residents of Charleston, West Virginia, and the hopeful prostitutes at the various fraternal lodges in the city, a war was raging on the screen before me. It was the late movie, *So Proudly We Hail,* a 1943 epic starring Veronica Lake and that heavenly Sonny Tufts. It was all about the courageous military nurses who served during those final fateful days on Bataan and Corregidor before they fell to the squinty-eyed, fingernail-pulling monkeys called Nips or Tojos or worse.

There was Veronica, sullen and morose because her fiancé had been killed by the Japs earlier in the war. The other girls didn't like Veronica in the movie. Claudette Colbert didn't like her. Neither did Paulette Goddard and Barbara Britton. But I liked her. I understood what she was going through. Not that I'd ever lost a boyfriend in a war, although I did have a beau break his leg in a football game and I plotted revenge on the fat tackle from the other team for months. Yes, I felt what Veronica felt. I felt it deeply. I was sure I would have reacted just as she did.

And then she made the big move.

"Don't do it, Veronica," I pleaded from the couch in a tightly controlled scream. I didn't want to wake my parents. "Don't do it."

But she did. She took that hand grenade, pulled the pin, and stuffed it down her fatigue front into the crevice of her bosom. Then, with head high, she walked slowly into the hands of those little yellow killers who were just waiting to get their bloodstained paws on so lovely a white woman.

"BOOOOOMMMMMM."

I jumped off the couch and ran to the kitchen. I dried my eyes with a Kleenex, filled my glass with more chocolate cream soda, and went back to the couch. I sat in stunned silence as the final few minutes of the film played out on the screen. Soon only memories and a test pattern remained. I couldn't go to bed, not in the emotional state I'd reached. I

8

drank the soda and finished the popcorn. And then I spotted it. The orange on the end table, the one snack I hadn't gotten to. I approached the table carefully and looked down at the orange sitting so alone next to last week's *TV Guide*. I reached down and carefully picked up the fruit with my right hand. Then, with equal care, I pulled the imaginary stem from its center.

"One, two, three . . ."

I shoved it down into the fold of my robe until it came to rest between my breasts.

". . . four, five, six . . ."

I walked slowly toward the kitchen. I could see them leering, drooling, gold sparkling from their teeth as they lustfully anticipated my arrival.

". . . seven, eight, nine . . ."

A smile came to my face. And the orange slipped farther down and fell to my stomach, the robe's sash keeping it from falling all the way to the floor. It tickled, and the Japs disappeared. I fished the orange out of the robe, ate it, and went to bed.

I had trouble sleeping that night. Would I have the guts to do it with a grenade, a real grenade? There I was in my second year of nursing school, and it all became very clear to me. Nursing the sick would not be enough to bring me true self-satisfaction. I would have to become a military nurse and spread healing to all the fighting men in every corner of the world. Besides, Charleston, West Virginia, is a dull town. Someday, when I returned with the medal and rode in the open convertible at the head of the parade, my people would know the contribution I'd made for a better, safer world for all to enjoy.

I awoke the following morning with an even keener sense of the call to duty. I couldn't contain myself. I stood with three classmates before the start of the catheter class and told them of watching the film and of my reaction to the hand grenade scene. Their reactions were disappointing.

"Boy, I bet that smarted when it went boom," one of them giggled.

"Only when she laughed," another equally insensitive girl snorted.

"I'd sure hate to lose what I have *that* way," a particularly buxom girl said grimly.

I eventually stopped thinking about that movie, but there were times during the following year that I would be reminded of it. Like when a date got fresh one night at a drive-in and reached down my dress front. I pushed his hand away.

"What's the matter?" he mumbled. "You got a bomb down there or something?"

Or when we played a game of Trivia at a party and everyone yelled in unison, "Sonny Tufts?????????????????"

That sort of thing.

I suppose I really can't give all the credit for my joining the Air Force to that motion picture. There were other, more tangible reasons for that decision. But you must admit that, deep down, the memory of an orange juggled precariously between my breasts played a large part in bringing me into the Air Force recruiting office in Charleston.

Jackie's reasons for joining the Air Force were quite different from mine. I realized that the first day we met in basic training.

"Did you ever see that movie, *So Proudly We Hail*, Jackie?"

"I never heard of it," was her reply.

"The one with Veronica Lake."

"You mean that actress with the hair drooping over one eye?"

"Yes, that's the one."

"I never saw any of her movies."

"Sonny Tufts was in it, too."

"Sonny Tufts?????????????????"

Despite the gap between us, Jackie and I became fast friends. We remained inseparable buddies as we blundered through the male world of the military, nursing the sick, upsetting the brass, and enjoying ourselves to the hilt.

"Why did you join the Air Force, Jackie?" I asked her the first night in the quarters we shared.

"It's just too awful to tell," she said quietly.

I didn't press, but my mind ran wild. Maybe here was a real, live Veronica Lake who'd lost an elderly beau in some faraway war. Or was she forced to leave her home town? What mistake in her young life had caused a whole town to run her out into the maverick world of the military nurse?

I didn't press for clarification because I didn't want to embarrass my newfound friend. And Jackie is Southern. I learned never to ask any question unless I'd cleared sufficient time for the answer. I never asked a question until my nails were polished, my hair was washed and set, letter written, and the sheets were turned back at the ready.

One night, after accomplishing these things and with nothing before me except bed, I again asked, "How come you joined the Air Force, Jackie?"

That night Jackie told me her tale. Jackie is a lovely girl, tall, blond, and warm, and when she speaks, the words and phrases come out in a languid, leisurely flow. To attempt to rush any answer would surely be criminal.

It seems that in Jackie's home town, a terribly tiny town deep in the bowels of Mississippi, there existed a secret organization about which Jackie had no knowledge until she dated Willard. Willard was a town boy who'd just returned from his two-year hitch in the Army and seemed to have become even more maladjusted than before he left. Jackie knew him only by sight, their distance in such a small community by Jackie's choice. Willard simply wasn't what you'd call the kind of boy you'd seek out for friendship. Naturally, Jackie was surprised when he called and asked her to a movie. She took pity on him and agreed to the date. That's the way Jackie is. She's very sweet.

After the movie Willard took her to a local root beer stand where they had tenderloin sandwiches and root beer in mugs. Willard hadn't said three words all evening, and Jackie was bored. She was about to suggest they drink up and head for home when he cleared his nasal passages, spit out of the window, and came to the point.

"I gotta admit, Jackie, that I'm here with ya 'cause of a certain mission I been assigned to carry out."

Jackie was confused. Her first thoughts ran to some childish male plot to ruin her reputation in the town. Jackie was known as a good girl with a sense of honor and decency. Had some nasty pack of boys assigned Willard the job of attacking her?

She looked over at him in the car and decided this fear was unfounded. If a pack of nasty boys *had* concocted such a plot, Willard would hardly be the warrior of their choice to attack the maiden. Maybe it was his nervous habit of picking his nose that created the credibility gap between chosen, ruthless lover and bumbling boy. Maybe it was his haircut—a home job in which all hair was sheared all the way up his head, stopping just short of a small circle of hair that perched on top. Maybe it was the fact that he called her "ma'am" a few times early in the evening that put her at ease. No, there was no need to fear aggression from Willard. She relaxed her grip on her high-heeled shoe and settled back in the seat.

"What mission, Willard?"

He spit again.

"Well, ma'am, it's just that some of the good ol' boys I hang with said you was thinkin' of joinin' the Air Force or somethin' like that. Boy, them guys are real mad."

Jackie was in her final year of nursing school at the time and had talked to the Air Force recruiter who'd set up shop for two days in town. She'd seen him late in the afternoon of his second day, and he'd confided in her that she was the only person who'd come to inquire about joining the Air Force. She didn't think much about this because of the town's small population.

"Who's mad, Willard?"

"Well, I can't rightly say, 'cept Bobby Joe Montrose is the most mad."

Jackie knew of the Montrose family. They lived in a hut on the outskirts of town, and Bobby Joe drank a lot. He had eight children, and it was rumored they'd taken to drink, too.

"How does he know I'm thinking of joining the Air Force?"

Willard spit and shifted through the gearshift quadrant four or five times before answering. Finally, safely in neutral, he blurted out, " 'Cause the guys took turns watchin' where that Air Force guy was them two days. Eacha us in the club took turns, and you was the only one who ever talked to that fella. The *only one,* Jackie Sutherland. And you a lady like. Oh, Bobby Joe is madder than all blazes, Jackie."

"But why should he be mad, Willard?"

"Now don't you go askin' me any questions. All I know is I'm supposed to warn you that you better not go doin' nothin' so foolish like joinin' the Air Force. That's all, ma'am. Just don't do it."

Willard slammed the gearshift in reverse and screeched out of the dirt parking stall, sending clouds of red dust into the open windows of every other car.

"You sonabitch," a teen-age boy yelled as the dust settled in his mug of root beer spiked with a stolen bottle of his father's bourbon.

Willard raced the car down the road and soon came to Jackie's house. He jumped out, ran around, opened her door, and stood at rigid attention.

"Jus' rememba what I said, ma'am. You jus' rememba."

Jackie recounted the evening to her parents at breakfast the next morning. She always felt free and easy discussing things with her parents. Both were understanding and interested in what their daughter was thinking.

12

Jackie told them what Willard had said, and her father burst out laughing. Her mother smiled and went back to the stove to fry more eggs.

"What's so funny?" Jackie asked her father.

Her father explained. It seems that Bobby Joe Montrose had returned home from his Army hitch to face an irate Mrs. Montrose. He'd had an affair with an Army nurse and his wife found out about it. To save himself, Bobby Joe claimed the Army had hired their nurses as prostitutes for the men. He even claimed this particular nurse had drugged him and forced him into their sexual relationship. Mrs. Montrose actually believed her husband and decided he should devote some of his energies to exposing the military plot of using nurses as women of pleasure. Bobby Joe went along with her request, partially because it would solidify his story and partially because he was beginning to believe his own tale.

He formed a secret society which he called the SSPDSB—Southern Society for the Prevention of Deflowering Southern Belles. His expressed purpose and that of the club was to keep young Southern girls from entering the Armed Forces. In addition, he talked of launching a national campaign of exposure of this military scheme.

"Bobby Joe Montrose is crazy," Jackie's father said. "He's a crazy lush."

After everyone stopped laughing, Jackie's mother turned serious. "What *are* you going to do about this Air Force thing, Jackie? We know you've looked into it, but you haven't told us of any decision."

Jackie had made up her mind.

"I'd like to join, Momma."

Jackie's mother cried, but her father smiled and came around behind Jackie's chair. He put his hands on her shoulders and said, "We're happy with any decision you make, honey. We have all the faith in the world in you."

They talked some more, and then Jackie went to the phone and called Willard.

"Willard, I just wanted you to be the first to know I'm joining the United States Air Force."

"Oh, damn, Jackie. Damn, damn, damn. Bobby Joe's gonna be madder than hell at me. I was supposed to make sure you didn't go and join."

"Well, you just tell Mr. Montrose not to worry. I promise to uphold the fine, noble traditions of SSPDSB."

Willard hung up. Jackie joined the Air Force. Her family

13

moved shortly after that to Colorado, where her father had accepted a good job with a large firm.

When she had finished telling me her story, I shook my head. "Why wouldn't you tell me the story before, Jackie? What's so terrible?"

"I don't know. I guess I was afraid it would sound sort of unpatriotic to have known someone in the SSPDSB. Besides, I sure wouldn't want any of these young handsome officers to think I'd start handing out literature every time we went on a date."

I understood. I wouldn't have wanted that, either.

Chapter 2

"Is It Too Late to Change Our Minds, Sir?"

An Air Force base in Texas.

Hot.

Dusty.

I got off the bus with my suitcases and stood in front of the gate to the base. This was to be my home for three weeks while I forgot about nursing and learned the basics of being a military woman. Beyond the gate stood various low, military-looking buildings, each possessing a temporary feeling. They huddled low to the ground, and I felt myself getting lower as I looked at them.

A beefy airman stood in front of the gate and just to the side of the gatehouse—a small concrete building that looked like any phone booth in Charleston. I'd been avoiding his eyes but finally looked directly at him.

"Can I help you, ma'am?" he asked in a crisp military voice.

I was flustered. I started toward him but had to go back for the suitcases I'd left behind. I grabbed them and half-dragged them to the gate.

"Yes. Yes, you can help me."

The airman continued to stare at me. He was at a proper parade rest, and not a muscle moved.

"Yes. You see, I'm assigned here. I'm a nurse." Then, as an afterthought, "And an officer."

He didn't really smile. It just seemed he did. He allowed his eyes to drop to my ankles, and he proceeded to scan me slowly right up to my hair—hair so carefully set before leaving home and now a mass of uncontrolled strands blowing in the Texas wind. I squinted against the yellow dust that swirled all around me and managed a weak smile at him.

"Orders, please."

"Orders?"

"Orders!"

He meant the orders I'd received assigning me to this base. I knew what he meant, but I couldn't pull my thoughts together concerning their location. I patted my white mini-idress for a pocket. No pockets. The guard stood at that same rigid parade rest; it was unnerving.

The suitcases. Of course. I'd put the orders in a suitcase. I didn't know which one contained them, but I took a chance on the smaller one. I opened it on the ground and rummaged through my clothing. There were no orders.

"I thought maybe they were in here," I told the airman.

"Yes, ma'am."

"Maybe they're in the other one."

16

"Yes, ma'am."

I opened the larger suitcase. There were the orders lying right on top of the clothing. I grabbed the papers, but unfortunately my fingers also grabbed hold of a pair of skimpy white lace panties. I brought up the papers and the panties just as an especially strong gust of wind came down the road. It caught the pants, and they sailed off toward the gatehouse. The airman didn't see them blow by and reached for the sheaf of papers in my hand. He took them and studied them carefully while I watched my best pair of pants flutter to a stop in the doorway of the gatehouse.

"Sir," I muttered, afraid to break his train of thought.

He didn't respond. He just kept studying my orders and grunting and frowning.

"Sir, my pants."

He looked up from the papers. Then he looked down to where all girls wear pants.

"Your pants?"

"They blew away. Over there." I pointed to the gatehouse.

He leaned forward a little the better to see my pants area. I suddenly realized the confusion in his mind and jumped in with, "Oh, no, no, no, no, no! I'm wearing my pants."

He turned scarlet.

"The white ones blew away. I'm wearing . . . Oh, forget it. I'll go get them."

I started toward the gate, but he quickly stepped in front of me. For a moment it seemed he'd decided I was pulling some dirty Commie ruse to gain illegal entry to the base. He bit his cheek and finally turned around. There were my pants in the doorway. He swayed back and forth a little in indecision before taking small, careful steps toward the pants. He reached them and stopped. He came to a tentative parade rest and looked down at them.

"They blew away," I yelled over the wind.

He bent down and gingerly lifted my pants from the doorway with his little finger. His hand came up slowly, the pants dangling from his finger like a flag of surrender. He again turned scarlet, and I detected a shudder that started at his feet and went right through his body.

Shudder over, he turned, and a silly grin broke over his pie face. He raised his arm, and the white panties fluttered high over his head. He was in this pose when the jeep roared around the corner of the closest building and came to a dusty stop just in back of the airman. A captain jumped from the jeep and bellowed, "AttennnCHUN!"

The airman's tongue came out of his mouth, and he gave the panties a little twirl as he spun around and faced the captain. The pants left his finger and flew directly into the captain's face. The captain violently shook them away and glared at the airman.

"What is the meaning of this, Airman?" he snarled.

"Sir, the lady's pants blew off and . . ."

The captain looked at me. I'm certain I looked like an Indian off the reservation looking for work. The dust blew all around me, and my hair hung down in sweaty hunks on my face, and all I wanted to do was cry.

"I'll take care of this, Airman," the captain told him.

"Yes, sir."

The captain walked over to me. He looked like a pale Errol Flynn or a pasty Douglas Fairbanks, Jr. His black moustache was thin on his lip, and his eyes were what are commonly referred to as bedroom eyes. He reached me and smiled a crooked smile.

"I'm Captain Ruttish. And you're . . ."

"Moura, sir. Lieutenant Joni Moura."

"Lost your pants, I see, Lieutenant."

"Oh, gosh, yes. They were in the suitcase and . . ."

"I know, Lieutenant." He yelled over his shoulder to the airman to bring my pants. The airman ran to us with them and handed them to the captain. The captain held them a little too long before returning them to me.

"Your pants, ma'am."

"Thank you, sir." I could have died.

"It's nothing, Lieutenant. Come on. I'll give you a lift to the Incoming Processing Center." He took my bags, and we climbed into the jeep and drove across the base. We pulled up in front of another low white building.

"Here's where you get off, Lieutenant Moura. Or may I call you Joni?"

"I guess Joni's fine, sir."

"Good. I'm Ted. I'll see you at Happy Hour."

"Happy Hour?"

"Oh, you have a lot to learn. And I'll be more than happy to teach you. The Officers' Club at five. See you there."

"Yes, sir."

"And please don't lose your pants again. At least not until tonight."

He grinned that crooked grin again. I blanched. Captain

Ruttish drove off, leaving me with the next unknown phase of my new life. I knew one thing, though. I didn't like Captain Ted Ruttish. I could picture him swinging in through my window at night, sword drawn and wearing those tight pants male ballet dancers wear. I decided I'd better be careful of Captain Ruttish and his sword.

Processing was a disappointment. All they did was tell me where I was to room. An airman took my bags and led me to the nurses' BOQ. He carried them up the one flight of stairs, his eyes in constant motion in the hope of catching a door ajar or a nude nurse trapped between rooms. Fortunately, he was disappointed in his dreams.

The room was comfortable, much more so than I'd anticipated. I hadn't expected to be alone in a room, but some basic wandering convinced me that was to be the case. My room was connected to another by the bathroom—a reasonable arrangement. I walked through the bathroom and into the adjoining room; the occupant had obviously been there and left. I went back to my room and decided a nap was in order after the long, hot ordeal of the day. A nap and a shower were just what I needed.

I'd no sooner gotten down to my underwear and stretched out on the bed when the door was flung open and a massive, muscular woman in fatigues stomped across the threshold.

"Well, well, Sleepin' Beauty. GET UP!"

I leaped off the bed and fell to my knees on the floor.

"GET UP OFF THE FLOOR!" she rasped, her hands on her linebacker's hips.

I managed to scramble up and assumed a reasonably straight position in front of her.

"What do you think this is, Lieutenant? A rest home for tired nurses? Get on a pair of slacks and a sweater and fall in in front of the building immediately."

The big woman swung around in a perfect about-face and marched from the room.

"Wow," I muttered as I threw open my suitcases in search of the clothing she told me to wear. Finally, dressed in tight slacks and tight sweater, I left the room and raced down the flight of stairs to the main entrance. I opened the door and was blinded by the brilliance of the sun, the dust, and the thick, oppressive sound of the big woman's voice again.

"Over here on the double," she screamed.

I ran to the sound, my arms flailing for balance. Then I could see again. The big woman stood in front of the flagpole that jutted up from the large area of burnt grass in front of the BOQ. Lined up in front of her were five girls, each wearing slacks and sweaters. They stood at attention, chests of varying sizes jutting out, fannies pulled in, hair blowing. I ran to the end of the line and joined them.

"I'm Captain Alantean. Marguerite Alantean. I'm going to be in charge of seeing to it that you girls shape up fast and become a credit to the Air Force Nurse Corps. Make no mistake about it, girls. I don't care how pretty you are or how big a bust you've got or how popular you were with the boys back in your home town. All I care about is how you shape up as nurses in the Air Force. For these three weeks you're gonna grovel for me. You're gonna forget you were ever pretty, dainty little things taking bubble baths and painting your toenails and having your hair done every week by some fag hairdresser. You're gonna hate me, and the more you hate me, the better officers you're gonna be. I've been shapin' up broads like you for eighteen years, and you'd better not cross me 'cause I intend to be doin' it for another eighteen. You just listen and keep your pretty little butts movin' and we'll get along. I never want to see any of you walk anyplace. RUN. Always RUN."

Captain Alantean stood back and allowed her words to echo over the hard ground and sink into our minds. She seemed satisfied at our total rigidity and lack of response. She was about to say something else when the girl at the other end of the line from me, a chesty blonde with long hair and a baby face, raised her hand.

Captain Alantean glared hard at her. "What do you want?" she snarled.

"May I be excused, sir?"

Alantean puffed up her cheeks and strode to the blonde. She stood two inches in front of her and made popping sounds with her mouth as her cheeks went in and out. The blonde smiled.

"Well, well, well. So you'd like to be excused. Just what you like to be excused for, little girl? Do you have to go to the bathroom?"

"Yes, sir, that's right."

"NO!" You could have heard her in Houston.

"But I have to go and . . ."

"No one has to go anywhere." Captain Alantean stormed back to her place by the flagpole. "You are not in school. You are preparing to go to battle. On the battlefield there is no time for raising your hand and asking to be excused. If you put up one finger on the battlefield, it will probably be shot off. If you raise two fingers on the battlefield, *they* will probably be shot off. If you put up three fingers on . . ." She realized she'd gone too far, and she stopped the lecture on battlefield bathroom facts of life. The blonde at the end stood with her lips and legs pressed tightly together. Soon she started jiggling around, and she finally said, "I just gotta go," and ran from her place toward the BOQ.

Captain Alantean stood shaking her head sadly. "Eighteen years," she muttered to the flagpole. "Eighteen years."

We all stood there wilting in the sun until the blonde came running back. "I have very weak kidneys," she apologized to the other girls in line as she took her place.

Captain Alantean was about to issue another proclamation when a Negro major came from around the back of the BOQ.

"It can't be true," he exclaimed as he walked to Captain Alantean. She saluted him, and he returned the greeting. "Captain," he said, "I cannot believe this. I simply cannot believe what I see."

"Believe what, sir?" Alantean asked.

"The obvious lack of readiness of these people under your command." He looked up at the sky and then back at Alantean. "Can't you see it's about to rain, Captain? Where are these officers' raincoats?"

We all sneaked a glance up. There was nothing but uninterrupted blue sky.

The major turned to us. "Can't any of you look up and realize we are about to be deluged with water?" he asked with exaggerated concern.

"No, sir," the blonde answered. The rest of us said nothing.

Captain Alantean pulled herself up to full height and shouted, "I'll have the situation in command, sir." Turning to us, she ordered, "You have ten seconds to get your raincoats on. GO!"

We all ran, but not before I saw the major wink at Captain Alantean. I felt better knowing they were having fun. I'd have hated to think they were serious.

Soon we were all back in line. We each wore our civilian raincoats, which added immeasurably to our discomfort in the heat.

"Button 'em up," Captain Alantean screamed. "Don't you know how to button a button, you dummies?"

We all buttoned our coats up to our necks.

21

"That's better. Now, let's see just how soft this generation really is. RUN! Around the area."

We all jogged in a big circle. We'd made three turns when the same Negro major came from behind the building again.

He did his double-take and told us to halt.

"Can I believe what I see?" he moaned. "Am I going mad? Is the sun making me crazy? Raincoats in such heat? Raincoats when the sky is blue and the nearest rain is in Miami?"

"Get those raincoats off, you dummies," Captain Alantean ordered. "I'm sorry, sir," she told the major. "They aren't too bright a group."

We all ran back with our raincoats to our rooms and returned to the flagpole area.

We ran around the area again.

The major came back.

We got our raincoats.

We ran.

Off with the raincoats.

On with them.

Two hours later, during a raincoat-on period, I collapsed on the ground. So did the other girls. We lay there in a London Fog heap and giggled. We rolled all over the ground and howled and laughed and gulped for air and totally lost control of ourselves. It was during this frolic that I met Jackie. We introduced ourselves during breaks in the snorting and giggling.

All this time Captain Alantean stood placidly with her hands behind her and a slight scowl fixed upon her face. We completely ignored her. But her presence became known again to all of us at about the same time. We sat up and peeked over at her, expecting the worst. But all she did was smile for the first time that day, shake her head, and mutter, "Eighteen years and they always end up on the ground giggling. Every time." She walked away and we went back to laughing.

Never before in the history of woman had a shower felt so good. I basked in the sting of the warm water and shivered with delight under the finishing cold spray. It was like going to heaven.

After showering and unloading my suitcases, I sat down in Jackie's room with a large Coke. I had expected to collapse into bed following our session with Captain Alantean, but once showered and safe from her for at least an evening, I found myself with renewed vigor.

22

"I feel so good," Jackie said, "I'd like to go over and try that Happy Hour I've been hearing about."

"Happy Hour. I was ordered to be there by a fading pirate named Ruttish."

"Captain Ruttish?" Jackie asked.

"The same. You know him?"

"Yup. I was checking in with the guard at the gate this morning when he drove up in his jeep. He gave me a lift to Processing, but he never mentioned Happy Hour."

"Captain Ruttish must spend his day hanging around the gate," I laughed.

"Official greeter," Jackie added.

"Lecher with bars," I threw in.

"Commissioned rapist." It was turning into a good game. I was about to say, "Headquarters heel," when there was a knock on the door. Jackie opened it and was greeted by the baby-faced blonde with the kidney problem.

"Hi," Jackie said. "Come on in."

The blonde introduced herself as Ginger Whip.

"I was gonna be a strip-tease dancer just 'cause a my name," she said sadly. "My parents were very cruel to name me that, don't y'all think?" she asked with big, rounded cow-eyes.

Jackie and I nodded.

"Excuse me," Ginger said. "I'll just use your bathroom for a minute."

While Ginger was in the john, another girl appeared at the door. She was thin and pale and wore wire-frame glasses. Jackie let her in, and she quickly launched into a story about the girl with whom she was sharing the bath. "I'm scared to death of her," she told us. "She's sick . . . up here." She pointed to her head.

"What makes you think that?" I asked.

This new girl, Sarah Parsons, told us she went to the connecting room to introduce herself to her bathroom-mate. She found the girl on her knees placing a horsehair rope in a circle around her bed. When Sarah saw the scene, she tried to back out of the room without the other girl seeing her. But her foot caught on the threshold, and she stumbled and let out a tiny shriek. The other girl jumped up and said, "What are you doing?"

"Oh, I'm sorry," Sarah answered. "I guess I stumbled."

"On the threshold?"

"Yes. Right here."

The girl wrung her hands and grabbed a wooden stick

23

from the table next to her bed. She came at Sarah and shook the stick three times in her face.

"What are *you* doing?" Sarah asked in a fright.

"Driving the spirits from your body. Tripping on that threshold was a bad bit of luck indeed. The Highland Scots knew full well what bad fortune that could bring. You must go back and enter the room again. Quickly. You haven't a moment to lose."

Sarah was afraid to disobey her roommate and did as she was told.

Her roommate smiled. "There. That's better. I was worried for you. My name is Marthas Trouble. What's yours?"

"Sarah Parsons. Did you say Marthas? With an 's'?"

"Yes. My parents named me Martha, but that has only six letters. Fortunately, Trouble has seven. But it's much safer to have both first and last names contain seven letters. So I had Martha legally changed to Marthas. Just being safe."

"Do you use an apostrophe?"

"Why would I do that?"

"For no reason."

Now Jackie asked Sarah, "Is she still in her room?"

Sarah shook her head. "She insisted I put a horsehair rope around my bed, too. It keeps the spirits away. She's out looking for one all over the base."

Everyone laughed except Jackie. Her expression became somber as she said, "I've never heard of a superstitious nurse. That's terrible. Think of the patients."

It was a sobering thought.

But it soon passed. The four of us—Sarah, Ginger, Jackie, and I—decided to head for the Officers' Club and an hour of whoopee at Happy Hour. We left the room, peeked out the building's main entrance for any sign of Captain Alantean, and walked to the low white building in front of which stretched a yellow awning in the best nightclub tradition— OFFICERS' CLUB. And standing in front, cigarette dangling from his lips, stood Captain Ruttish.

Chapter 3

"You Can't Afford Not to Drink"

The Officers' Club was very impressive. You first entered a large lobby in which pictures of missiles, airplanes, and insignias lined the walls, relieved only by photographs of the top brass of the base. There was little doubt who was the base commander. His photograph stood slightly alone in the center of the wall, the other photos separated by a respectable amount of pale green wall space. The commander, a general, looked down with stern black eyes on all who crossed the threshold of the club. You were almost compelled to take out your ID card and flash it at him before venturing from the lobby into the bar or dining room.

The bar was to the left of the lobby. Huge leather-covered doors separated it from the other rooms; you couldn't hear a murmur from it until you pushed the doors open and entered.

But the moment you did enter, you were assailed by a sheet of sound. The bar was six deep. The tables were crowded together and filled to capacity. Two frantic waitresses tried to keep up with orders from the tables, their constant screaming soprano notes on top of the predominantly male din.

Ruttish led the way to a wall position at the far end of the bar. The trip through the maze of men was a hazard for any self-respecting female. Ruttish would open up a hole, but it would immediately close just as one of us was halfway through. Twice I caught the full force of heavy elbows or fannies as they caught me in a squeeze. There was usually an apology, and I'd acknowledge it with a faint, painful smile.

Jackie didn't fare any better. But Ginger seemed to suffer the worst crush of all. Well, maybe "suffer" is the wrong word. It soon became evident that she was lingering in those moments of masculine rumpling. She bit her lip every time her very ample bosom and rear end were compressed, and she let out a coy, "Oh, my," and giggled as she maneuvered into the next impossible situation. She finally reached us and said with great Southern sincerity to Ruttish, "Oh, my, what a fine and wholesome-lookin' group of men. Everyone looks like an officer *and* a gentleman."

Ruttish sneered.

"Well, let me give you some good advice," he said in a whisper. "Every one of these guys would pull your pants down as soon as look at you. Good soldiers, yes. But they have no respect for a woman. All they'll want from you is whatever selfish pleasure they can get. You'll have to be extremely careful around here. Frankly, I think you'd be wise to stick

26

close to me, at least for the first few weeks. Until you become used to things. You all look like fine girls, and I'd hate to think of your first weeks in the Air Force as unpleasant ones. Just stick close and I'll get you through."

Jackie looked at me and I looked at her, and it was a struggle to suppress the laughter. Sarah took his words to heart and cowered closer to the wall. Ginger gently touched his arm and said, "I think I know what you mean, Captain Ruttish. And thank you."

"Call me Ted."

At first we assumed we were the only females in the club. But that wasn't true. Through the haze we could see six or seven others at various tables. Most were our age, although there were two who looked as though they'd been around for a while.

We all ordered whiskey sours except Sarah, who asked for a Horse's Neck. The bartender at our end, a pale, bald sergeant working on his off hours, shrugged at the request. "Next thing they'll have the junior prom here," he muttered under his breath as he grabbed the ginger ale bottle.

"I read once that military people drink a lot," Sarah said as we sipped our drinks. "More than the average occupation group. Do you find that true, Captain Ruttish?"

"No. Not at all. As a matter of fact . . ." He stopped in midsentence as he glanced at the men lined up at the bar. "Well, yes, it is true. That's part of the problem you must beware of. Hard-drinking woman-chasers. Be on your guard."

Sarah was. The rest of us said nothing until Ginger smiled at Ruttish and said, "I wouldn't wonder if it was true. Why, drinks are so cheap here you can't afford not to drink. I just love whiskey sours."

"I do, too," Ruttish said. "It's a proper drink. Have another."

We all had another round of 45-cent whiskey sours, with Sarah reluctantly joining us in a devil-may-care second Horse's Neck. She soon dropped out of the party and headed back to the BOQ for a night's rest. We all sensed her hesitation in going back through the gauntlet of male elbows. She finally drew herself up to her full height and pushed through, her arms held in a cross of protection across her flat chest.

By now Captain Ted Ruttish was having trouble holding his own against a growing wave of lust at the bar. No one approached us for the first half-hour. But soon officers started drifting toward us. Ruttish was clearly concerned. A handsome young captain came over and said, "Hey, Ted, they don't allow harems in the Air Force."

"Ha, ha, ha," Ted replied, his mouth turned down at the ends.

A bald lieutenant came right over to me and asked me to join him for dinner. I declined. After all, I didn't want to offend Ruttish. Jackie was feeling the same limitations. But we shouldn't have been so sensitive. Ruttish had already decided Ginger Whip provided his best chance for an evening of romance.

"Does Ginger bite?" he asked her with a silly grin on his face.

"No, silly," she giggled back. "But Ginger snaps."

God, how they laughed! I accepted the next dinner invitation I received. So did Jackie. We went to a table as a foursome, leaving Ginger to lean up against Ted Ruttish, who ordered another round of drinks.

We sat down just in time for the band to begin playing. It was a trio of piano, bass, and drums, each musician an airman from the base band who earned extra money at the Officers' Club. It was good music, so good that the club had signed them for five nights a week throughout the summer. Naturally, military etiquette dictated that the musicians could not join anyone at a table or at the bar during their intermissions. It was a shame because the piano player was cute, much more so than my dinner companion, a paunchy major with bad breath. Jackie had fared better; her date was a rugged fighter pilot in for the night from his base somewhere in New Mexico. He was leaving the following morning for the East Coast.

Dinner was quite good. The major was good company if you could manage to keep your head slightly turned away from his mouth. The fighter pilot was casting a certain spell over Jackie, and the evening developed into an enjoyable one.

Ginger and Captain Ruttish had, after many drinks, taken a table by themselves directly in front of the trio. Both were obviously drunk, the primary tip-off Ruttish's constant offering of dollar bills to the piano player for playing World War II love songs. He played them all, and Ruttish played the role of the downed pilot having a final dinner with his French love before leaving through the underground network to return to his unit in England. The amusing thing was that

28

Ginger had fallen into the drama and was performing the French girl's part to perfection.

After dinner people started dancing and singing along with the musicians. Everyone except Ruttish and Ginger. They sat at the table, his hand covering hers as he crooned the same World War II songs to her that had been played an hour ago. He was oblivious to the music of the moment.

They closed the club at midnight, and our dates walked Jackie and me back to our BOQ. Both were perfect gentlemen, and after a pleasant round of goodnights, Jackie and I went to our rooms. A sudden wave of fatigue swept over us, and we were both in bed ten minutes after undressing and using the communal bath. It had been a long, hard day, and I fell asleep not sure whether I was wearing my raincoat or not. As for Jackie, as she recounted it the next morning, she went off wishing she had a horsehair rope around her bed to keep Captain Alantean away forever.

Chapter 4

"We May Become Officers but Never Gentlemen"

It's known that your deepest sleep comes during the first four hours of slumber. To be awakened during this period is brutal, cruel, and detrimental to one's central nervous system. As nurses, we were well aware of the need of proper sleep for general well-being.

But it was hard to display any professional understanding the next morning when, at 4 A.M., Captain Alantean strode through the halls of the BOQ yelling, "Up, up, UP!" Our reaction was purely personal.

Jackie came racing through the bathroom and into my bedroom.

"Oh, my God, oh, my God," she moaned. "What'll we do?" It was obvious she thought we were in the midst of an air raid or Indian uprising.

"Get up. That's what we do," I mumbled, rolling out of bed. "Get up and do some silly thing, I guess."

"I'm going to write my Congressman," was Jackie's answer as she found her way back to her own bedroom.

There's an awful panic at a time like that. I absolutely could not make a decision as to my first course of action. But the brown taste of the Officers' Club made up my mind. I found my toothbrush and went to the sink. I looked into the mirror and closed my eyes against the monster that looked back at me.

I brushed hard and was almost finished when the pounding started on my door. I ran to it and opened it. Standing before me was a girl. She was easily six feet tall, and her shoulders stood out from her neck like two pieces of twelve-inch oak shelving. Where they ended began a straight line down to the floor. It was like looking at a human packing crate of flesh and muscle. Her face followed the geometric lines of her body. Her hair was short. A crew cut.

"The captain says you're late," she mumbled in a foghorn voice. "You're supposed to be outside now."

"We just got out of bed," I protested. Box-Body blinked against the inadvertent spray of Crest that came from my mouth.

"She said *now!*" The hulk spun around clumsily on her right heel and marched up the corridor toward Jackie's door. I slammed my door shut and ran to warn Jackie. It was too late. I reached her bedroom just as she was opening the door to Box-Body. Jackie stood there as the identical message was mouthed by the hulk. When it was over, Jackie closed the door, turned around, and started crying. "Willard was right," she sobbed.

"How was he right, Jackie? He said you'd become a prostitute. All you've become is a gym teacher. At this rate who'd have the energy to be a prostitute? Come on. Let's get outside."

We threw on the same slacks and sweaters as the day before and raced into the hall. We were joined there by Sarah Parsons, who came limping down the corridor from her room.

"What happened to you?" I asked as we headed for the stairs.

"That kook next door found a horsehair rope for me. I got up and tripped over it this morning. Some good luck she brought me!"

It was pitch-black outside. The heat was already beginning to displace the cooler night air, and the crickets all seemed to be laughing at us from behind bushes.

Alantean stood tall next to the flagpole. She was dressed in fatigues and wore a fatigue cap. She watched us fall into a line, and her face reflected a distinct attitude of scorn.

"Get that line straight," she bellowed.

We tried.

"It has been fifteen minutes since you ladies were awakened," she said in a sugary, sarcastic voice. "Fifteen minutes. In fifteen minutes the enemy would have overrun this base and killed every patient . . . and *you*."

We looked around. There were no enemy to be seen, nor were there any patients facing any danger of annihilation. Only crickets.

"In the future," Alantean went on, "you will be in formation within six minutes of wake-up. Six minutes. Anyone later than that will be subject to discipline. Is that understood by all?"

A few of us muttered.

"Am I understood?" she screamed.

"Yes, sir."

"I am not a sir. I am a ma'am."

"Yes, sir, ma'am."

"What am I?"

"A ma'am."

It wasn't easy to accept.

"It looks like you all need a little waking up," Alantean said flatly. "Ten laps around the pole."

"How cruel, how brutal," Jackie gasped after the first lap. I nodded my agreement, trying to preserve precious breath.

"I can't go on," Jackie wheezed after the fifth lap.

"You've got to," I said. "Remember SSPDSB." My reminder seemed to have a positive effect on my friend. She was running stronger on the sixth lap.

No one spoke on the final laps. It was just a matter of putting one wooden leg in front of the other, one numb thigh to lift after the other. No interest in anything but survival . . . and Ginger Whip. Ginger was obviously in very good physical shape. She ran the course with long, sure strides. And she wasn't wearing a bra. Ginger was an amply endowed young lady, and every stride brought about an obvious and large-scale jiggling under her pale pink sweater. We all watched her out of the corners of our eyes as a matter of interest at the physiological ramifications. It had always been my experience that performing any physical activity *sans* bra was an unpleasant situation. It slowed you down, at least.

But Ginger ran on into the pale light of a peeking sun, her bosom proudly bouncing and a hint of a smile on her face.

Interest in Ginger wasn't confined to her fellow runners. Captain Alantean also watched with interest. Finally, the running over, Alantean barked, "Whip. Here on the double."

Ginger ran to the captain. They engaged in a heated, whispered discussion that none of us was able to hear. Ginger then left Alantean and ran to the BOQ. When she returned a few minutes later, her bosom was securely throttled in a bra. She didn't look at all happy.

Ginger's return marked the end of our rest period. We proceeded to do an undetermined number of push-ups, which Ginger did with vengeance, some sits-ups, squat-jumps, and toe-touches. It was uphill all the way.

It seemed likely that calisthenics were now over and we would be dismissed. But those hopes appeared dashed when Jackie raised her hand and asked permission to speak to Captain Alantean. The captain told her to step forward, and Jackie did as she was told.

"Well, Sutherland, what is it you wish to say?"

"Well, ma'am, it's just that, as a nurse, I wonder if all this exercise is good for some of the girls. I mean, what if one of them has some physical ailment or something like that? This exercise could be harmful. Why, studies have shown that violent and prolonged exercise for those not accustomed to such activity could bring on serious harm to their health. I remember reading one such study in which the doctor said . . ."

It took Jackie a long time to get that statement out. She

34

chose each word carefully and delivered it in her slowest drawl. I must say Alantean showed great patience in listening to the full statement.

". . . and so, Captain Alantean, I conclude by asking your consideration in this matter." We were tempted to applaud but checked the impulse.

Alantean nodded her head in a gesture of understanding. Jackie stepped back into line and looked pleased. A cricket chirped. Alantean spoke.

"Dismissed!"

Everyone congregated in Jackie's room and sang their praises of her. It was much like a locker room scene in which the player who's just scored the tie-breaking touchdown during the final few seconds of the game is being given hero attention and love. Jackie sat quietly and modestly, pleased but humble. We hadn't met most of the girls in the room, and everyone started introducing themselves to one another. Soon the room had taken on a party atmosphere, despite the early morning hour: 5:30 A.M.

Marthas Trouble sat on the arm of the couch and joined in the aimless chitchat. She seemed, at least to me, a nice normal girl who was just one of the gang. I realized this wasn't so, however, when the girls started singing.

" 'For she's a jolly good fellow, for she's a jolly good fellow, for she's a jolly good fellow . . .' "

"STOP!"

It was Marthas. She'd jumped up off the couch arm and stood in the middle of the room, her arms outstretched in a silencing gesture.

"You don't know what you're doing," she said with passion. "It's only five-thirty in the morning. If you sing before seven, you'll cry before eleven. Sing before you eat and you'll cry before you sleep."

Marthas walked gloomily from the room. The rest of us sort of fumbled our way back to our own rooms to prepare for breakfast, which, according to the book of rules we'd been given, was to be eaten each morning at six.

After all of us had left, I went back into Jackie's room. She sat where I'd left her, her mouth going as she recited Marthas' little sayings.

"Do you think it's true, Joni?" she asked.

"What? About crying before sleep and all that nonsense? Don't be silly. That girl's a nut and you know it. Come on, hero. Grab a shower and we'll eat."

"OK, Joni. Say, you don't think she sticks pins in dolls and things like that, do you?"

"Don't be silly. Not in this day and age."

Not in this day and age.

Chapter 5

"Sam, You Made the Pants Too Long"

While the rest of us ate breakfast at the Officers' Club, Marthas Trouble sat in her room making little dolls from rags and clay. She sat cross-legged on her bed, her fingers working feverishly with the materials. Soon she'd fashioned two little dolls, each with a tiny body wrapped in cloth, and large, oval clay heads still to be formed and painted into recognizable people. Satisfied that she had made progress in her project, she placed the dolls in a dresser drawer and took one last, loving look at her handiwork. The two featureless dolls lay there like eggs waiting for the Easter dye. Marthas closed the drawer, left the building, and went out to her car. She just had time for a quick breakfast before the group's first scheduled activity—the fitting of uniforms.

Most of the girls had taken the bus to the club. Few of them had driven to the base, although many had cars at home. The bus trip lasted four minutes, just enough time for a few of the girls to fall asleep. The group was under the direct supervision of Sergeant Emily Morrose, now more commonly known to us as Box-Body. She sat lumplike in the front of the bus and said nothing to anyone. The bus driver, a skinny airman with freckles, greeted her with a friendly military greeting but was promptly rebuffed by Box-Body's foghorn "Hurmpf."

Ginger Whip was the only girl at breakfast displaying any measure of alertness. She ate heartily and smiled at everyone, especially some male officers seated at nearby tables.

Eventually the good food and hot coffee brought everyone around to better spirits. Laughter began to displace the gloom, and we left the club ready for anything the day might bring, including Captain Alantean. Ginger continued to be the most exhilarated. She proclaimed as we left the club and hit the morning air, "I feel just great. There's nothin' like exercise to get the juices flowin' and the blood runnin'." She breathed deeply and touched her elbows behind her back. "I went steady with a football star once, and he taught me lots of exercises." She giggled. "Why, would you believe I was once only a thirty-six?"

"NO," Sarah Parsons replied with mock shock. "That's amazing."

"Yup. A thirty-six. Then Tom got me doin' all those marvelous push-ups and made me touch my elbows like this, and I just grew and grew."

"Wow."

Ginger grinned. "That's why I got so mad at Captain What's-her-face this morning."

"You mean because you weren't wearing a bra?" I asked.

"Yes. How did you know that was the problem, Joni?"

"We guessed. What did Alantean tell you?"

"It's really very vulgar. I shouldn't even repeat it."

"Come on, Ginger," Sarah urged. "You can tell us. We'll understand."

"Well, as long as you understand I don't usually talk this way. You *do* understand?"

"Yes, we do."

"That vulgar officer told me to bottle up my boobies or she'd do it with bandages."

We all snickered except Marthas, who'd arrived in time for juice and a Danish. She responded by making three arcs in the air with her hand. Then she climbed on the bus and sat alone in the back.

We drove to the outer perimeter of the base, and there, next to a supply hut, stood a small store covered with signs. One large master sign dominated the store's front. It read: UNIFORMS OF PARIS. Under the big sign was a slightly smaller one, reading: SATISFACTION GUARANTEED. And a still smaller one, reading: WELCOME LADIES AND GENTLEMEN OF THE ARMED FARCES (sic).

Box-Body led us inside the store. We were greeted by a tiny, bald man who introduced himself as Mr. Abraham Lefkowitz, Tailor to the Military. His partner was also introduced by Mr. Lefkowitz. "This is Harry," he said. "He's my partner." Harry smiled and fastened his eyes on Ginger.

"All right, ladies," Mr. Lefkowitz said, rubbing his hands together. "Who's the lucky lady to be first?"

Ginger giggled and stepped forward. "I heard you should never volunteer for anything in the military," she said. "I used to go steady with a fighter pilot. That's what he told me. But I'll try anything once."

She started to follow Mr. Lefkowitz through the curtains at the rear of the store, but Harry jumped between them.

"I'll fit you," he muttered.

"I must warn you you won't have an easy time fittin' me. I have a very unusual figure, Mr. . . . . Mr. . . . ."

"Call me Harry. I'm a partner."

Ginger went through the curtains as Mr. Lefkowitz sputtered a feeble protest. He stopped Harry as he started to follow Ginger into the back, and whispered in a very loud voice, "Keep your hands off, Harry. Remember last time. Just keep your hands off."

"OK, OK."

39

Mr. Lefkowitz looked directly at Jackie and said, "How about you, young lady?" Jackie went with him, leaving the rest of us to browse among the many uniforms on display.

"Don't touch nothing," was Box-Body's advice.

The uniforms weren't bad, all things considered. The white mess dress uniform was the nicest, and the blue-and-white pin stripe wasn't bad. The fatigues were fatigues. What can you do with fatigues? There was also a display of shoes that brought forth reactions from some of the girls. The center of attention were the black granny shoes that made no attempt to break with the past.

"You wouldn't catch me dead in those," a pretty brunette said as she picked up a granny shoe and turned it over a few times. "They'd make my calves look like bowling pins."

"You'll wear 'em," Box-Body grunted. "You'll wear 'em or go barefoot."

"I'd rather go barefoot."

"Hurmpf," Box-Body snorted.

"Hurmpf," we snorted back.

Ginger returned about ten minutes later. She was all grins. Harry, the partner, came out a few seconds later after being heard to say behind the curtains, "Thirty-eight. Yeah, Lefkowitz, thirty-eight for real."

Mr. Lefkowitz was heard to reply as Jackie came through the curtains, "Thirty-one, Harry. For real. But so what? This is a business, not a house of flesh."

Both smiled politely as they came back to lead two more of us into the fitting rooms. Sarah Parsons went with Mr. Lefkowitz, and I went with Harry. As soon as we were in the fitting room, I said to Harry, "Thirty-four. For real." He grinned an embarrassed grin, revealing very yellow teeth.

I could hear Sarah and Mr. Lefkowitz in the next room. He said to her, "You ready?"

"I guess I'm ready, Mr. Lefkowitz."

"Hokay." He whipped the tape measure from his neck and flipped it around Sarah's hips.

"Hmmmmmmm," he went as he slipped the tape up around her waist. "Hmmmmmmm," as the tape went around her bust. "Hmmmmmm."

"Not so good?" Sarah asked.

"What's good? You got three places worthy of measurement like everybody else got three places. In all three places you could use a little more to measure. You could use a little more behind you and a little more in front of you. But who's to say what's good? Maybe you got a boyfriend, huh? Maybe *he* should say what's good."

"He likes me," Sarah responded weakly.

An hour later all of us had been measured. Marthas Trouble was the last to go, and it wasn't long before an argument broke out with Mr. Lefkowitz.

"I don't want any buttons on the sleeves or the back," Marthas could be heard saying.

"Buttons? A thousand years the Air Force has been defending the country and you worry about buttons."

"I will not have buttons. They are nothing but a place for the devil to hang on to."

"Devil schmevil. Raise your arms, or do you want your bust measurement to include your elbows? Devils. Buttons. I only pray I should not get sick and have you as my nightingale."

On the way out of the shop Mr. Lefkowitz gave us a farewell speech.

"It has been the pleasure of Abraham Lefkowitz and Uniforms of Paris to serve each of you. Tomorrow your uniforms will be ready. And remember. We guarantee satisfaction."

"Hurmpf," Box-Body said as Harry added, "If you have any problems, see me, Harry. I'm a partner." He seemed to be speaking only to Ginger.

We left a waving Mr. Lefkowitz in front of his store and bussed to the base hospital. A terribly cute second lieutenant met us at the entrance and escorted us to the staff conference room. We were served coffee and sat chatting until a colonel entered the room. He was quite distinguished-looking and carried his silver-gray hairpiece with style and dignity.

"Good morning, ladies," he said, peering over his half-frame glasses. "Welcome to one of the finest medical facilities in the Air Force Command. I'm Colonel Rogers, hospital commander. You'll be spending a good deal of time here during your three-week training period. Hopefully, that time will be spent as students and not as patients. But, should you come down with some ailment or other, rest assured we'll be ready to serve you.

"There's a possibility that some of you will find yourselves assigned here permanently after training. For those of you who do, I'm confident you'll find things comparable to those civilian institutions in which you trained and worked. It's our mission here to bring your civilian nursing training into coordination with established military rules of conduct.

You're part of well over a thousand people currently going through some forty courses in various areas of medicine. In all probability many of you will go on to the six-week course for flight nurses, which I can assure you is a worthwhile and stimulating experience.

"I'm going to introduce you now to your course supervisor who'll be directly responsible for you during this three-week period. Captain Richard Monoman."

Captain Monoman had been waiting in the wings, so to speak, and he made his entrance upon mention of his name. Colonel Rogers left the room, and Monoman stood before us in a stance of fear and suspicion. He was a short, chubby man with thin hair and piercing little black eyes that darted in rapid circles as he looked at you. Marthas leaned over to me and whispered, "Don't look directly at him, Joni. He's got the evil eye."

I avoided his gaze from that moment forward. He cleared his throat a dozen times before attempting to speak. Finally, in a sudden burst of breath, he said, "Hi."

We began clearing our throats in sympathy. It seemed to help.

"I'm Captain Monoman, your course supervisor. And I'll be in char-char-charge of you while you're here."

His eyes started doing circles again as we sat in our seats staring at our new leader.

"Are there any questions?" he asked with a tremor in his voice.

It was assumed, especially by Captain Monoman, that there would be no questions. This would have held true except for Marthas who, obviously and suddenly stiffening in her chair, raised her hand.

Monoman gnashed his teeth in anticipation. He'd opened his uniform jacket a few moments earlier, exposing his waist. He pushed his hands hard into his belt and took deep breaths.

"Y-y-yes?"

"Your belt, sir."

Monoman grabbed his belt buckle and tugged on it, looking down as he did so. He also did a fast check of his zipper—closed, to his relief.

"Wh-wh-what about m-m-my belt?"

"Isn't it an eel belt?" Marthas asked.

"Eel? Ah, yes, it is. I . . ."

"Is that regulation, sir?" she pressed.

"W-w-well, no. You see . . ."

Marthas sat back in her seat and let out a long, satisfied sigh of pleasure. Then she got up and walked up to Captain Monoman. She offered her hand, and he took it as one takes a hot piece of charcoal from the grill.

"I understand," Marthas said with warmth.

Monoman was getting frantic.

"And your name, Captain," she said. "Is it really Monoman?"

"Dismissed," Monoman blurted, his face red with anger and shock. "Dismissed. Th-th-they're yours, Sergeant Box ... Sergeant Morrose." He stumbled from the room, his hand at his throat, his tiny black eyes revolving in their sockets like out-of-control roulette balls.

"I knew it," Marthas shrieked. "I knew it."

"This way," Box-Body said.

"Knew what?" Jackie asked as we sat firm.

"Hurmpf," Box-Body grunted.

"Knew he was a kindred spirit," Marthas bubbled. "Imagine that. An eel belt. And his name. Obviously taken from Monomania, meaning one believing in supersitition. Seven letters. Count them. And Richard, too. Seven letters. I'd never have believed I'd meet someone like that in the Air Force. I was sure I'd be doomed to years of solitude in my beliefs, but here he was—a fellow believer."

Box-Body stood in the doorway with a mean expression on her square face. We all got up and followed her to the lobby of the hospital. Marthas continued bubbling as we walked down the hall. She was obviously a girl in love.

"What a marvelous man," she said over and over again.

"What about those evil eyes?" I asked.

"Only for nonbelievers," she answered quickly.

We passed through the lobby and were walking to the bus when Monoman came running out the door behind us and headed for the parking lot. Marthas wheeled around and grabbed his arm in a viselike grip. It brought him to a devastating halt. Marthas looked directly into his circling eyes and smiled. Then she reached into the pocket of her sun dress, took something from it, and placed it in his hand. Letting go, she watched him as he threw a fast, worried salute and continued toward his car.

"What did you give him?" Sarah asked once we were settled in the bus.

"A worry stone. An Indian worry stone. I suppose none of you know anything about them, do you?"

We agreed we didn't.

"I have others," Marthas said. "I'll teach you about them and let each of you have one."

"Thank you, Marthas," we all said. "That will be very nice."

We were at lunch at the club when Jackie thought to ask about the significance of the eel belt. Her question brought forth an enthusiastic answer from Marthas, who seemed genuinely pleased that someone was showing interest in what was obviously a very important part of her life.

"It's very simple," she explained. "An eel belt is worn to keep rheumatism away from the wearer. The idea came from New England and has proved itself to be a very worthwhile and effective prevention." There was a strong inner need to argue the point with our superstitious classmate, but no one did. Marthas sat back in her chair and smiled. "I wonder if Captain Monoman will be at the club tonight. We have so much to talk about."

Chapter **6**

"Only the Physically Fit Shall Endure"

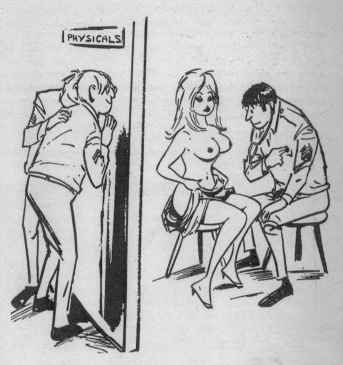

Ginger Whip was the star at the physical examinations that afternoon. The corpsmen—those enlisted men working in various medical areas—were obviously quite taken with the initial sight of Miss Whip. She sat there with us in the Sick Call waiting room and bulged at the seams for all who would pass by. She was also full of offhand comments like "I tickle so easy," and "I hope the doctor warms the stethoscope before he uses it [giggle-giggle]." All this chatter delighted the corpsmen, who seemed to be constantly busy passing Ginger's chair on their way to some urgent mission.

"I went steady once with a medical corpsman," she told all of us. "And do you know *he* used to do the exams on new female recruits at his base? Of course, they were just enlisted girls. I'm sure we'll have a very high-rankin' and professional doctor exam us. Oh, I do hope his hands are warm. I get chilled so easily."

We waited a full half-hour under the watchful gaze of Sergeant Morrose before a nurse came out and told us we'd be having our physicals in just a few minutes. We were each given a questionnaire containing all the pertinent medical questions the doctor would want answered before he actually examined us.

Everyone seemed a little nervous about the exam except Ginger who, despite her coy little statements of apprehension, seemed to be ready and anxious to leap off the chair at the call of her name. Jackie and I sat talking about how everyone becomes nervous before a physical exam, a fact that isn't altered in any way by a nurse's knowledge and exposure to this sort of thing. All of our hearts were beating just a little bit faster, and no matter how we tried to dismiss thoughts of the exam, there was still the dry mouth and sweaty palm to remind us we were about to be probed, felt, listened to, and, in general, evaluated for our physical attributes and failings. Human nature for all people, including nurses.

We went to work on the medical forms, some honestly, some shading their answers to present a better and healthier picture than was the case. The form was as on the following page.

The filling out of forms completed, we sat nervously waiting for our call to be examined. The airmen continued to stroll past Ginger, their eyes doing quick takes of her crossed legs and pulsating sweater. Ginger was making her usual impression on them.

CLINICAL EVALUATION

NOR-MAL	(Check each item in appropriate column; enter "NE" if not evaluated.)	ABNOR-MAL
	18. HEAD, FACE, NECK, AND SCALP	
	19. NOSE	
	20. SINUSES	
	21. MOUTH AND THROAT	
	22. EARS—GENERAL *(Int. & ext. canals) (Auditory acuity under items 70 and 71)*	
	23. DRUMS *(Perforation)*	
	24. EYES—GENERAL *(Visual acuity and refraction under items 59, 60 and 67)*	
	25. OPHTHALMOSCOPIC	
	26. PUPILS *(Equality and reaction)*	
	27. OCULAR MOTILITY *(Associated parallel movements, nystagmus)*	
	28. LUNGS AND CHEST *(Include breasts)*	
	29. HEART *(Thrust, size, rhythm, sounds)*	
	30. VASCULAR SYSTEM *(Varicosities, etc.)*	
	31. ABDOMEN AND VISCERA *(Include hernia)*	
	32. ANUS AND RECTUM *(Hemorrhoids, fistulae) (Prostate, if indicated)*	
	33. ENDOCRINE SYSTEM	
	34. G–U SYSTEM	
	35. UPPER EXTREMITIES *(Strength, range of motion)*	
	36. FEET	
	37. LOWER EXTREMITIES *(Except feet) (Strength, range of motion)*	
	38. SPINE, OTHER MUSCULOSKELETAL	
	39. IDENTIFYING BODY MARKS, SCARS, TATTOOS	
	40. SKIN, LYMPHATICS	
	41. NEUROLOGIC *(Equilibrium tests under item 72)*	
	42. PSYCHIATRIC *(Specify any personality deviation)*	
	43. PELVIC *(Females only) (Check how done)* ☐ VAGINAL ☐ RECTAL	

NOTES. *(Describe every abnormality in detail.*

"My, they certainly do work hard here, don't they?" Ginger said with wide eyes.

"My, they certainly do," Jackie answered, carefully not looking at me.

We didn't have to wait much longer. One of the airmen came to the door leading into the inner offices and said, "Miss Whip. This way, please."

Ginger got up and twisted around into what she considered to be an acceptable clothing arrangement. She fluffed her hair, lifted her chin, and flounced out after the airman.

"I have a feeling her whole life's been one big physical," one of the girls commented. No one cared to debate that statement.

Ginger was led to a small room in which a table stood against the wall. It was surrounded by boxes of varying sizes and shapes. The airman closed the door behind them and scanned the clipboard he held in his hands, his manner highly professional.

"Well, Miss Whip, the doctor will be along in a minute to exam you. In the meantime will you please undress and put this on." He handed Ginger a nylon hospital gown that was at once flimsy and small. She held it up in front of her and frowned.

"I'm afraid this is goin' to be much too small," Ginger demurred.

"Well, Miss Whip, we've been fighting with supply for months, trying to get a new issue of gowns. But that's the Air Force for you. You'll just have to make do with this one."

"Oh, my," Ginger sighed. She looked up at the airman, and he understood her look.

"You can get undressed right here, ma'am. I'll be back when you've finished."

"Thank you." The airman left the room and Ginger went about removing her clothing.

In the meantime another airman had come to the waiting room and told all of us to follow him. He led us to a large, professionally equipped examining room that contained a scale, a wall-hung sphygmomanometer, an assortment of stethoscopes, cabinets filled with tongue depressors, thermometers, cotton balls, hypodermic needles, ear-eye-nose-throat flashlights, and a carton of filter cigarettes. One of the nurses came in and handed us each a heavy white cotton hospital gown and told us to get undressed and wear the gowns for the doctor. We were in the process of doing this when Sarah realized Ginger wasn't with us.

"Where's Ginger?" she asked. "Why isn't she in here with us?"

No one had any answer. But everyone's imagination ran wild.

In reality, Ginger had finished undressing in her private examination room and was trying to adjust the abbreviated nylon robe to cover the expanse of her body. And while she valiantly worked at this task, the airman who'd led her into the room and his friend, a skinny little airman with huge glasses and long hair, stood on the other side of the wall, their eyes glued to two tiny holes in the wall that were strategically located to allow a clear field of vision between the boxes.

"An incredible specimen," the skinny fellow whispered to himself. "Incredible." The other airman said nothing. He just kept pushing closer to the hole.

"I'd better go in before she gets wise," the skinny one muttered to his buddy. "Shhhhh."

Airman Regents, the skinny airman, knocked on the storeroom door.

"Come in," Ginger said.

Regents entered, a stethoscope around his neck, a clipboard in his hands.

"Hello," he said with professional calm and detachment.

"Hello, Doctor," Ginger answered.

"Well, let's see," Regents continued. "Please sit on the table. Sorry for the mess of this room, but we're very crowded here at the hospital."

Ginger jumped up on the table. The nylon gown slid right up to her hips, and Regents did his best to avoid direct and obvious stares.

"Oh, my, Doctor, but this silly gown just wasn't made for me."

"Yes. Well, we'll start with your pulse and heart."

Regents nervously took Ginger's wrist in his fingers and counted silently as he looked at his watch. That completed, he placed the stethoscope in his ears and fumbled the conical listening device against Ginger's chest.

"Hmmmmm," he muttered. "Would you please drop the top for me?"

Ginger giggled coyly.

"Come now, Miss Whip. As a nurse you certainly can't be bothered by usual medical procedures, even when they apply to you."

"Of course not, Doctor. Not professionally, anyway. It's

just that I've always been a terribly shy and reserved girl, and I guess my upbringin' and values sometimes get in the way [giggle-giggle]."

"Yes, of course. Please drop the top."

Ginger did as she was directed, allowing the gown to come over her shoulders and fall to just above the classic line of motion picture decency. Her arm held the gown from falling any farther.

"Hmmmmmm," Regents murmured as he placed the stethoscope at various spots across the tops of her breasts. "A little lower, please."

Ginger removed her arm and the gown dropped into a heap on her lap. Regents stood with his mouth open, the stethoscope poised in mid-air inches from Ginger's chest. She looked down at it as it stood there motionless in front of her. Regents' eyes were locked onto the sight of her large, firm bosom that jutted out before him.

"Jesus H. Christ," could barely be heard from behind the boxes as the other airman tried to burrow his right eye farther into the wall.

"What?" Ginger asked.

"What what?" Regents said nervously.

"I thought I heard someone, Doctor."

"No, no. Impossible. You may put your top back up, and I'll be back in a moment."

Regents left the storeroom. Once the door was closed behind him, he darted into the adjoining storeroom where his buddy stood.

"Shut up, you idiot," Regents whispered in disgust.

"What a pair," was the only answer he received.

"Keep your big mouth shut, you creep." Regents went back to Ginger's room, where she sat demurely on the table, the nylon gown once again tied at the back of her neck.

"Well, now, let's see, Miss Whip. Heart and pulse seem fine. Fine at the rest position, that is. Now, if you'll get off the table, we'll do some exercises to check your heart's reaction to strain. Would you please jump up and down on one foot for me? And maybe you'd better take off your gown so I can observe general muscle tone and physical condition."

"Jump up and down without my gown?"

"Yes, yes. That's right."

"I just couldn't do that, Doctor."

Regents snapped his heels together and assumed a dictatorial air. "I'm afraid I don't have time for argument from you, Miss Whip. You're in the Air Force now, and the command of a superior is to be obeyed."

"Oh, my," Ginger sighed as she untied the gown from her neck and let it fall to the floor. She picked up the gown, placed it on the table, and looked at Regents. "Should I start jumping now, sir?"

"You bet. I mean, yes, you may begin."

Ginger started hopping up and down on her right foot just as our real doctor came into the big examining room where the rest of us sat waiting. He was a young, good-looking captain.

"Good afternoon," he said in a crisp military-medical tone. "We'll make this as quick and painless as possible." We all smiled at this good news except Marthas Trouble, who sat rubbing her Indian worry stone with vigor.

"Let's make sure we're all here," the doctor said. "Call the roll, Airman." The airman referred to had, up to this point, been busy sorting out the forms we'd filled in outside. The doctor's command brought the airman up straight in his chair.

"Uh, sir," he said, "I have to get the master list outside. I'll be back in a minute."

The doctor looked annoyed. He nodded his reluctant approval of the airman's proposal. The airman left immediately.

"Well, I guess we'll have to wait for the master list," the doctor muttered. "I like to do things in order. Do things in order and you don't make mistakes."

Once outside, the airman ran down the hall and turned into the storage room next to the room where Ginger was hopping up and down.

"She's on her left foot now," Regents' buddy said, his eye leaving the hole in the wall for only a moment.

"Lemme see," the other airman demanded. He pushed Regents' buddy away from the wall and pushed his face against it. "Ain't that great," he said to himself. Then he tore himself away and looked at the other airman. "Come on. The doc is about to call the roll, and we gotta get this broad back in there with the others. Get Regents outta there."

"OK." The other airman went to the door of Ginger's room and knocked. It panicked Regents, who had just suggested that Ginger stop hopping and lie down on the table. He went to the door and opened it a crack.

"They started the real exam, Regents," his buddy told him.

"Yeah. OK."

Regents went back to Ginger.

"All right, Miss Whip," he said in as professional a tone as he could muster under the pressure of the moment. "This phase of the exam is done. You can rejoin the others now." His tone *was* professional, but his open-mouthed, wide-eyed look was at odds with the tone. He stood there gaping at the voluptuous female lying before him. Ginger had adopted one of those classic nude poses so popular with models posing for murals to be used over men's bars.

"Perhaps I'll see you again, Miss Whip," Regents said. "Now, put this robe on. Hurry up."

Ginger got up from the table and took the robe Regents handed her. It wasn't the flimsy nylon robe she'd worn previously. It was a heavy cotton robe, just like the ones the rest of us were wearing.

"Here you go, Miss Whip. These just came back from the base cleaners. Now you run on down to room eleven and join the rest of the girls there. And by the way, I'm instructing you to say nothing of this phase of the exam. We have very rigid rules here about any divulgence of anyone's individual medical history. It could be a very serious offense, serious enough to bar your commission into the Air Force. Understood?"

"Yes, sir. You've been very kind, Doctor. I'll see you again soon."

"Yes, that's right. Now hurry to room eleven. Hurry now."

" 'Bye-bye, Doctor."

" 'Bye-bye, Miss Whip."

Ginger sort of skipped down the hall and entered room eleven where we were all gathered. The airman had returned and slowly read off what he'd termed his master list.

"Hurry up, Airman," the doctor snapped. "We're falling behind schedule. Schedules must be kept."

"Yes, sir."

Ginger's entrance brought everything to a halt. She tiptoed through the doorway and smiled at the doctor as he turned at the intrusion.

"My, I guess I'm a little late," she said.

"Yes, you are. Where have you been?"

"Well, I was . . ."

The airman cut her off. "We had the patient flow set up, sir, and it went a different way than planned." He went right back to reading off the names. The list ended with Ginger.

"All right, we can finally begin the physical," the doctor sighed. The airman breathed an even deeper sigh.

"You may leave now, Airman," the doctor told him.

"Yes, sir." The airman left the room. Once outside, he ran around the corner and entered a janitor's supply closet that stood just on the other side of the examining room's far wall. Regents and his buddy were there.

"Come on, come on," his buddy was saying as he tried to pull Regents away from the wall. Two cans of disinfectant had been pushed aside on the shelf to allow Regents' head to fit in between and press against the wall.

"What're they doin' now?" his buddy asked.

"He's going to start the heart listening. Shut up, big-mouth. You'll get your turn."

No one in the room noticed the tiny hole in the wall that intruded just to the right of a medicine cabinet. We all dropped the tops of our robes as the doctor walked along, stethoscope to his ears, and listened to our respective hearts. He stopped to comment only when he came to Ginger.

"You have quite a rapid heartbeat, Miss . . ."

"Whip. Ginger Whip, sir. It must be from jumpin' up and down."

"Jumping up and down?"

"Yes, sir. You know. First on one foot, then on the other. Like this." Ginger started jumping on her right foot.

"Stop that."

"Yes, sir. But the other doctor said . . ."

"I don't care about other doctors. *This* doctor doesn't have people jumping around examining rooms like some tennis ball. Don't ever do that again, Miss Whip."

"Yes, sir."

The boys in the broom closet breathed a deep breath of thanks.

The doctor was very efficient. He whipped through the rest of the physical in record time. When he'd finished, he curtly told us we could get dressed, and he and the nurse left the room. The door closed, we took off our hospital gowns and started reaching for our clothes. We were all in a sort of naked charade pose when the door opened and the airman who'd been there originally stepped into the room.

"Coming through," he barked. "Everybody close their eyes."

We all *did* close our eyes while he sauntered past us, his eyes taking in everything. It was Sarah Parsons who realized the absurdity of the situation and yelled, "What are *we* closing *our* eyes for?" By that time the airman had passed through and disappeared through another door.

"I think we've been taken," Jackie muttered as she dressed.

"What about you, Ginger?" I asked.

"What about me?"

"Where were you?"

"The same place you were. Getting the first phase of the exam."

"The first phase?"

"Yes. That stupid doctor we had in here sure doesn't know very much. The other doctor who examined me and took the readings before and after exercise was a lot smarter than this guy. Who'd you have for the exercises?"

It was obvious Ginger had been taken a lot worse than we had. "Oh, another doctor on staff," I answered. "They have so many doctors around here."

"My, they certainly do. I just hope they're all not as stupid as this one." With that, Ginger snapped her bra over her bosom and did a few elbows-behind-the-back movements to keep things the way they were.

Chapter 7

"God Is Alive and in the Air Force"

Our last stop for the afternoon was the base chaplain's office. It was located in another low white building beside which stood the base chapel, an A-frame that would have been perfectly at home at some ski area. It was devoid of any religious decoration, the two tiny stained-glass windows above the door the only hint of things religious that might go on inside.

We got out of the bus and entered the building behind the hulk of Box-Body. Once inside the hallway, we were confronted with three doors. The door at the far left had a sign above it that read: Jewish. To the far right was a door and its sign: Catholic. And immediately in front of us was an open door and its sign: Protestant.

The big, red-faced chaplain in the Catholic office came out into the hall just as two other chaplains emerged from their offices. They all stood before us, smiled, and issued very cordial greetings. We were returning their greetings when Box-Body broke things up with, "All right. Protestants in the middle, Jews to the left, and Catholics to the right." We all shuffled into groups as called for by her order. Well, all of us except Ginger and Marthas. They sort of stood between the groups.

The chaplains ignored those of us who'd committed ourselves and drew individual beads on the two without obvious affiliation.

"You can come right in here with us," the Catholic priest said with a broad grin. "No obligation, of course. Just sit with us."

"Your parents?" the rabbi asked Ginger and Marthas. "Would they have a preference for you? I'm sure they would. Feel free to join us if only for this afternoon."

"Oh, my," Ginger said, her hand covering a little giggle. "I've never been the subject of such attention."

"Have you ever been affiliated with a church, young lady?" the Protestant chaplain asked.

"Well, not really, although I was engaged once to a Baptist preacher. Actually, I suppose you could call me a freethinker."

"Right this way," he said with finality. "You belong with us. And you?" he asked Marthas.

"Astrology, although I have dabbled with Bibliomancy and Capnomancy." The Catholic priest shuddered and led those of his faith down the hall and into his office.

"Well, we don't have any chaplains representing any of those ... ah ... faiths ... specifically," the Protestant said

56

with kindness. "Perhaps the good rabbi here might better understand your beliefs than I do."

The rabbi became indignant. "Why me?" he said. "With all the offshoots in your area of responsibility, maybe this cockamayme thing you . . ."

"Capnomancy," Marthas corrected him.

". . . yes, that's what I'm talking about. Maybe my good friend here who represents everything else has a place for you."

"Now wait a minute, Rabbi," the Protestant said with a certain edge to his voice. "I've got plenty of those who used to be with you. Don't forget that, my good rabbi."

"Don't worry about my ever forgetting anything like that. I know the way you work. I know the way you woo them away with all your free love and sexy sermons and the like. I know."

"Gentlemen!" the priest bellowed from his office. "Please."

"I'm sorry to be causing all this trouble," Marthas said quietly. "Actually, I'd rather not be part of any of these religious groups."

There was stunned silence on the part of the chaplains. The priest came out of his office and gave Marthas a severe look. The rabbi looked skyward as the minister forced a smile. Finally it was the Catholic chaplain who broke the silence.

"God may be dead where you come from, young lady, but he's still a member of the United States Air Force."

"But I didn't mean to imply that God was anything like dead. You see, it's just that my background and beliefs are so . . ."

"I think you might be happier with me," the minister said after some soul-searching. "I'll take both of the uncommitted ones," he said to his colleagues.

"It figures, it figures," the rabbi muttered as he led his group down the hall to the left.

The meeting with the Catholic chaplain was a rather straightforward and predictable one. He told his girls of his recent experiences as chaplain at the Air Force base at Dhahran, Saudi Arabia, in which the practice of any religion other than Islam was prohibited.

"I've returned with renewed faith," he told the girls. "After spending eighteen months hiding my priesthood under the guise of being listed as base recreation officer, I've come to realize how important it is for each of us to stand tall and proudly proclaim our beliefs."

"Did you hold Mass?" he was asked.

"Yes. But only in the theater and with guards at the doors. And with wine smuggled in from a nearby island in the Persian Gulf. You'll never know how degrading it is to be known as recreation officer number two, as opposed to my Protestant counterpart who was known as recreation officer number one."

"It all sounds very exciting and romantic," one of the girls commented.

"It was humiliating," the priest replied.

"Did you also really act as the recreation officer, Father?"

"Yes." His face was a deep red now as his anger grew with memory. "I was Santa Claus at an undercover Christmas party. And I was in charge of the base badminton tournament. The language!" He shook a little.

Meanwhile, to the left, the rabbi was holding court for those girls of his faith.

"He's writing a book," one of them told me after the meeting. "He's antiwar and wants to end the draft."

The meeting of the Protestant group lasted the longest. The minister, a young, fiery Unitarian, spent the greater part of the meeting discussing pornography and the evils of censorship.

"Frankly," he told his flock, "I'm in some trouble here at this base. I addressed a local women's club three weeks ago and instead of talking on the subject of morality in the military, I drifted off onto this subject of pornography."

"Didn't they like that? The women, I mean?" one of the Protestants asked.

"Not at all. I'd been instructed by the base CO to assure each of them that morality was higher than ever in the Air Force and that they could be proud of the boys. Sort of appease their fears about having some of the airmen date their daughters. But I got carried away. I told them so what if their daughters experience sex at an early age. We're a nation of hypocrites. We're a nation of suppressed and neurotic sexual animals striving for relief. That's what I told them."

"Good for you," Ginger snapped. "I agree."

"I do too," he answered without thinking.

There was a painful void until he finally brought up another subject.

"I'm also in a bit of trouble because of my Congressional lobbying activities."

"What do you lobby for, sir?"

"Many things. Civil rights. Housing. Our crowded skies. But the one thing that riled the brass here was when I tried to push a bill requiring that all military Protestant chaplains be Unitarians."

"All of them?"

"Of course. It isn't in the budget to have Methodists and Lutherans and Baptists . . ."

"All of them?"

"I used to be engaged to a Baptist . . ."

"Yes, you told me, miss. Now, as I was saying, you can't expect our government to have on hand chaplains from every offshoot Protestant faith, now can you?"

"Absolutely not." It was unanimous.

"So the Unitarian faith embraces all. Right?"

"Of course."

"Frankly," he went on, his voice becoming more and more confidential, "I'd like to see the rabbi go. And the priest, although I'm sure that will never come about. There's strength up on top *there*, you know. At any rate, my lobby seemed perfectly logical. But other religious groups complained, and now I'm in the doghouse around here."

"What a liberal man," Ginger said with reverence.

"It's the only answer," he concurred.

"And what of me, Mr. Liberal?" Marthas said sleepily. "Where do I fit in in this scheme with my unorthodox views of the supernatural?"

"I'll have to think about that." We ended the meeting, and I assume he did just that. In fact, we saw him sitting hunched over martinis at the club for the better part of that night.

Chapter 8

"TGIF"

The following morning, Friday, began as had the previous day. We fell out at 4 A.M. for calisthenics and found the ritual more difficult than the previous morning. This despite Jackie's assurance upon going to bed the night before that things would be better.

"The first day of exercise is always the most difficult," she said, and I believed her.

But Friday morning proved her to be misinformed on such matters. It was brutal as Box-Body stomped through the halls, her fists beating on doors and her earsplitting voice echoing from every corner of the building.

"Nooooooo," a weary female voice was heard in protest.

"Just ten minutes more," Jackie moaned from her bed.

"Not one second more," I answered as my feet hit the floor. "Remember, it's going to be easier."

"You've got to learn never to believe me," Jackie muttered as she made it to a sitting position.

Ginger Whip got up and vomited.

Sarah got up and again tripped over the horsehair rope.

"Take this rope out of here!" she screamed at Marthas.

"You'll be sorry," Marthas scolded as she wrapped the rope in a neat circle.

We were all out by the flagpole in ten minutes—four minutes above the standard set by Alantean the day before.

"Well, well, well," she began. "Still can't manage to bounce out of that bed and get with it, can we? Still content to allow the enemy to overrun the post while you catch a few extra winks. I suppose you sat at the Officers' Club and sipped your drinks and made chitchat just like you did when you were civilians back home. All this while innocent patients are slaughtered by an enemy that goes to bed on time and takes *its* work seriously."

How could we?

"Little defenseless children at the mercy of barbarians," Alantean continued with sadness in her voice.

Punish us. For we knew not what we did.

"And as a cruel and ruthless enemy violates our women, loots our homes, and destroys our freedom and self-respect, one of you comes to me yesterday pleading for leniency and understanding." Alantean's eyes focused on Jackie. "She comes to me and asks that I take it easy because some of you might not be fit to run a little or bend a little or sweat a little. Well, well, well."

I actually felt a momentary anger and disgust for Jackie.

How dare she? And then I snapped back into the reality of the early hour and the fact that no one had been raped or looted, to my knowledge. I looked at Ginger, and the sly smile on her face might have indicated something along the lines of rape. She'd spent the evening at the club with Captain Ruttish and who knows where else after they departed around eleven. Maybe there had been rape. Maybe Ginger had raped Ruttish. But Alantean wasn't speaking of that kind of rape. She was obviously setting us up for some devious and difficult punishment for Jackie's sins. She went right on to a clarification of what that was to be.

"So, ladies, I think it's time to instill a little sense of responsibility in your mission here. Sutherland. Step forward."

Jackie made a couple of false starts before actually taking steps toward Alantean.

"Yes, sir . . . ma'am."

"You are in the United States Air Force, are you not, Lieutenant Sutherland?"

"Oh, yes, ma'am."

"And the United States Air Force is dedicated to superiority of the air, is it not?"

"Yes, ma'am. That it is."

"Well, then, we'll have to see just how superior we'll be with you a part of the team. Moura. Front and center."

I was shocked. Why me? I went to Alantean and stood at attention beside my roommate and friend.

"I believe it's safe to assume that you, Lieutenant Moura, as Lieutenant Sutherland's roommate, are probably the most likely to be influenced by her words and thoughts. Does that sound reasonable?"

"No, ma'am. What I mean is . . ."

"What *I* mean is that you are the most likely to be influenced by her words and thoughts. Does that make sense now?"

"I guess so, ma'am."

"We don't guess at anything in the Air Force."

"It makes sense, ma'am."

"Good. I knew it would."

I knew it would, too. I knew it all along.

"Get the engines, Sergeant Morrose," Alantean commanded Box-Body. We watched her march to a jeep nearby and come back with four medium-size electric fans. She handed Jackie two of them, and I received two.

"These are aircraft engines, ladies. They make the aircraft a flying and potent weapon when they're turning at full speed. From this moment forward, each of you is a twin-engine aircraft. Your mission is to fly as fast and as long as you can. At least longer than enemy aircraft. Take off!"

Jackie and I started running around the flagpole, a fan in each arm.

"What are you?" Alantean yelled.

"Twin-engine aircraft," we answered in unison.

Ginger started giggling as we completed our first turn around the pole. It was a mistake on her part.

"Whip. You're a glider, and you'd better make sure you keep flying."

Ginger fell in with us. Soon Alantean had the others running with us. She eventually called a halt to the agony, and we concluded the session with push-ups, sit-ups, and toe-touches. There was no party atmosphere as we filed back to our rooms for showers. No one said a word except Marthas, who mumbled something that sounded like dialogue from *Tarzan's Great Adventure*.

As we climbed aboard the bus that would take us to the Officers' Club and breakfast, Box-Body handed us a printed sheet outlining the schedule for the rest of that day and the weekend:

```
0700—Breakfast
0800—Films—(Military Etiquette)
              (Personal Hygiene)
              (History of the Air Force)
1030—Uniform pickup
1045—Uniform refitting
1200—Lunch
1300—Class—(Military Etiquette)
1400—Class—(Personal Hygiene)
1500—Class—(History of the Air Force)
1600—Interview—(With Base Information Officer)

SATURDAY
0800—Inspection of facilities
0900—Tour of base.
1100—Free until 0400 Monday
```

There was, however, a note at the bottom that said:

64

All officers are expected to attend worship at the church of their choice.

[Signed]
RUFUS GIDDYPATE
General, USAF

We all thought it was strange to assume that the uniforms wouldn't fit. It was defeatist, at least. Jackie asked Box-Body about it.

"Nothin' Lefkowitz and his partner ever makes fits," she snorted.

"Then why are they allowed to be the tailors on the base?" I asked.

" 'Cause that's who the general wants."

"General Giddypate? The base commander?"

"Positive."

Drew Pearson-like thoughts began to flash through my brain. A kickback? Blackmail? In the family?

"Well, why does General Giddypate keep them here if they do bad work?" It seemed a perfectly logical and in-order question. But Box-Body simply snorted and walked away.

The movies after breakfast were terrible. The film on etiquette was a series of vignettes in which a single airman did everything wrong in matters of proper military behavior. It was very grainy and had obviously been chopped up a great deal over the years, much like the movies on TV where someone's hand suddenly jumps from his pocket to his nose with no motion in between. There was some giggling at the star of the etiquette movie who seemed very gay in his walk and manner. He had a habit of allowing his little finger to protrude from his saluting hand which had evidently been overlooked by the brass screening the film.

The film on personal hygiene was obviously an attempt to upgrade those films we watched in the third grade. A homely WAF brushed her teeth in graphic close-up that seemed tasteless and slightly underground; was this the way Andy Warhol began his cinematic career? This same girl rubbed deodorant all over herself and spent an interminable amount of screen time washing her hair. She performed nail care for our benefit and took a shower and sprayed something on her feet and in her shoes. This film was newer, and the vivid color heightened all the lack of taste that went into its making. At the conclusion of the film the girl stood proudly while her date, the same gay airman from the etiquette

65

movie, picked her up in front of her barracks. They walked off arm in arm as the narrator, also held over from the previous movie, intoned, "A cleaner *you* is a happier *you*. The Air Force is proud of you. Be proud of yourself."

Then came the history film. It was a series of still photographs that were given some movement by the zooms and pans of the motion picture camera. The same narrator talked of how far the Air Force has come since its inception as a branch of the Army many years ago. There was a lot of march music played and sounds of airplanes taking off and machine guns going *rat-tat-tat-tat-tat*. We never really did see the whole film because the projector went haywire toward the end and the airman running it seemed confused. He finally apologized to Box-Body, who answered him with a garbled stream of abuse at his incompetence and stupidity.

We climbed into the bus for the trip over to Uniforms of Paris. We were quite excited at the prospect of picking up our uniforms. This was a sort of official moment for each girl; uniforms seemed to be the most tangible example of our new careers.

Abraham Lefkowitz came running out of the shop to greet the bus. He threw his arms open wide and said, "Welcome back, my dears. Every one of you is going to look like a queen, believe me. I guarantee it. Remember what I said. We guarantee satisfaction."

Harry slouched behind the counter as we filed into the shop. He perked right up when he saw Ginger, and she played up to him with coy smiles and sly giggles.

"My goodness," she cooed to him, "if you've managed to fit me right the first time, you'll be the only man ever to have done that. I have a very unusual figure and . . ."

"You should all try on your uniforms now," Mr. Lefkowitz said, "and then we'll take a look at all of you. Sometimes we need to take in a little here, a little there. Just a stitch maybe. To be perfect. You should all be perfect."

None of us turned out to be perfect. My skirt on the pin stripe hung from me like a potato sack. Harry's creative tailoring resulted in Ginger's jacket fitting like a straitjacket. The buttons threatened to pop any second as her chest strained against the jacket front. Her fanny all but burst from her skirt, which was pulled in tight against the back of her legs.

"A little stitch here, a little stitch there," Lefkowitz said with great joy and happiness. "The final touches necessary for perfection."

Harry refitted Ginger while Mr. Lefkowitz took care of the rest of us.

"In a day or two your uniforms will be delivered directly to your rooms." Lefkowitz held up his hand to stop protest that had never started.

"It's nothing. Nothing. It's all part of the service of Abraham Lefkowitz to the United States of America and its lovely young nurses. And believe me, goils, in all my years fitting uniforms for young ladies in the Air Force, I have never been so fortunate to serve such a beautiful group of young ladies. Beauty queens, every one of you."

Only Ginger took it to heart.

"Why, thank you, Mr. Lefkowitz. I once won a beauty contest in my home town. It was sponsored by the Chamber of Commerce, and, my, was I surprised when they said I was the winner! I remember I wore the cutest and . . . well, it was skimpy for someone like me . . . but I think they liked it. I was going steady then with one of the biggest men in that Chamber, and it was he who encouraged me to enter the contest and . . ."

"Everybody back in the bus," Box-Body bellowed.

" 'Bye, Harry."

"I'll see you tonight, Miss Whip," Harry answered. "Tonight."

"Till then."

"If she went with as many fellas as she claims," Jackie said as we settled in our seats, "She'd have to be eighty years old."

"Or holder of the world's record for one-night romances."

"Can you imagine," Jackie went on, "making a date with that horrible Harry?"

"Don't forget he's a partner."

"He's also a creep."

"A creepy partner."

Lunch was lunch.

And then we attended the classes that would expand on the films we'd seen earlier in the day. The officer who taught the class on military etiquette dwelled on the proper relationships between officers and enlisted personnel. Ginger asked whether we could fraternize on our off hours.

"It's especially bad on off hours," the teacher answered. "That kind of casual situation does great harm to necessary military conduct."

"What a shame," she whispered to Marthas. "I think that piano player at the club is kinda cute."

67

A female lieutenant taught the course on personal hygiene. She was very good and very enthusiastic. The only problem was the credibility gap caused by her dirty fingernails. You just couldn't have faith in what she was saying.

Air Force History was dull. The history itself is really very exciting, but the entire session consisted of looking at slides of the same still photographs used in the motion picture.

Finally, at three-forty-five, we left the classrooms and headed for the interviews with the base information officer. We asked Captain Alantean, who joined us after the classes, what the interviews were about.

"Publicity. That's what they're about," she responded.

It all sounded very exciting. Sort of Broadway and big-time. We went to the interviews brimming with enthusiasm.

The base information officer smoked a pipe. He wasn't very old, maybe thirty-five, but he was almost totally bald and frowned a lot. How he managed to achieve a tweedy look in his uniform was a question we still can't answer. But he did achieve that look, and he knew it.

"Good afternoon, ladies," he began, pacing the floor in front of us and playing little finger games with his pipe. "I'm Captain Penner. I'm the information officer here at this base, although I'm really a novelist."

We all reacted appropriately, and Captain Penner paused for the reaction. He spoke again before anyone could ask what novels he'd written.

"It's my mission to tell the story of the Air Force and its people to the outside world. Up until recently this was accomplished in a very routine and dull manner. But the new Air Force is very much aware of the need for new techniques for communication. I suppose that's why they feel a novelist can bring new dimensions to the job." He laughed. We did, too—nervously.

"So we're going to go about the job of telling everyone back home about you and your new careers as nurses in the Air Force. Airman Kraus here will distribute forms for you to fill out. He'll answer any questions you may have. I'm going back and bat out a few pages while you're working on the forms. I'll be back in about fifteen minutes."

He gave us a little salute with his pipe and left the room. The pie-faced airman handed us the questionnaires. He seemed very nervous over being alone in the room with so many girls. Or maybe it was Sergeant Box-Body who unnerved him.

We went to work filling out the forms.

68

Captain Penner reentered the room fifteen minutes later and took the forms from Airman Kraus. He shuffled through them, occasionally chuckling, mostly scowling, and always fiddling with his unlighted pipe. He eventually pulled one form from the batch and looked up over it at us.

"Lieutenant Trouble."

"Yes, sir."

"Trouble. That's a rather unusual name."

"I don't consider it unusual, sir."

"No offense, Lieutenant. But with your first name, it strikes me as different and unusual."

Marthas stiffened and her lip curled in defiance. Penner continued to look at her over the form she'd just completed. We all shuffled a little in our chairs and cleared our throats. It seemed an eternity before either of them spoke again. It was Captain Penner who broke the silence. He waved his pipe in the air and tilted his head to one side.

"Well, let's not be overly sensitive, Lieutenant Trouble. It's just the old novelist in me rearing his ugly but inquisitive head. I guess none of you have ever known a novelist before. If you had, you'd understand the nature of the beast. We're always probing. We never just accept what's on the surface. It's second nature to look at the world and understand it. Without doing that, we'd never be able to write it like it is."

Marthas didn't answer. She sat there rubbing her Indian worry stone with her right thumb while her left hand opened and closed on the metal amulet hanging on a chain around her neck.

Penner wisely went on to another of the forms.

"Miss Whip?"

"Oh, my. Yes, sir."

"I see here you were a beauty contest winner."

"Why, I wasn't even going to put that down, but I thought I should answer every question truthfully."

"Yes. That's good. Honesty. Too many writers today aren't honest. Honesty rare as a man without self-pity. Stephen Vincent Benét. But I'm sure you've never read him."

"Oh, but I have." The voice belonged to another girl in the group who hadn't said two words since we arrived at the base. Her name was Sybil Longstreet, and she roomed with another quiet girl named Penny Pross. "I've also read the poetry of his brother, William Rose Benét. Have you?"

It was obvious Captain Penner hadn't read anything by the brother, but he wasn't about to make that admission. "Ahhhh, yes. William Rose. Brilliant. We'll have to talk further sometime." He looked through the forms. "And what is your name?"

"Sybil. Lieutenant Sybil Longstreet. Perhaps I've read some of your books, sir. I read a great deal."

It was the wrong thing to say. Captain Penner reacted just as Marthas reacted when challenged. He stiffened and squeezed his mouth with his fingers and slapped his pipe against his thigh.

"Well, perhaps, Lieutenant Longstreet. We'll ... ah ... ah ... discuss it at another time."

Penner pulled a cigarette from his pocket and lighted it.

"Well, now. We'll prepare news releases to your hometown papers. That's Airman Kraus's job here. Good hard news releases. And ... ah ... I'll give some thought to more in-depth feature stories. Once you have your uniforms—and they fit—we'll get some photographs. Eight-by-ten glossies and like that." He choked a bit while inhaling his cigarette. "So, in the words of Jerome K. Jerome, leave-takings are but wasted sadness. Let me pass out quickly." He had started to make a dramatic exit from the room when Sybil Longstreet stopped him with, "I believe the proper ending is ... let me pass out *quietly*."

"Yes. Well ..." He fished another cigarette from his pocket and tried to light it. "Well, we'll be talking again." Penner left the room.

Captain Alantean informed us we were dismissed and free to take the bus back to the BOQ. We all decided to walk directly to the Officers' Club which was just across a mall from the information officer's building. The only dissenter was Marthas. She took the bus back to her quarters, and, as we proceeded to create a TGIF (Thank God It's Friday) party at the club, Marthas sat on her bed fashioning another doll to add to her collection. Her fingers deftly worked with the tiny clay head until it began to resemble Captain Penner. She even carved a minuscule pipe from wood and attached it to the cloth arms of the doll. That completed, she carefully placed it in her drawer along with the other two dolls which did not, as yet, have any recognizable facial features.

She joined us two hours later at the club and seemed to be in the best mood of her life. Captain Ruttish was there and, upon seeing Ginger with Harry, the partner, proceeded to descend upon Marthas. Strangely enough, she reacted favorably, and soon they were dancing cheek to cheek and swaying in one spot while the beat went on. A few times I noticed Ruttish's hand slip down and gently pat Marthas' rear end.

70

Jackie told me after we got back to the BOQ that Marthas was doing more patting than Ruttish. Evidently there is no superstition against fanny patting, which was encouraging to a lot of people at the club that night.

It was a marvelous party. Drinks were two-for-the-price-of-one until seven o'clock, and we all took advantage of the sale.

By ten o'clock things had disintegrated into a gay holocaust.

By eleven a large percentage of the party people were beyond help.

And at midnight only the heartiest of souls remained on their feet. Marthas had departed with Captain Ruttish, Ginger and Harry were nowhere to be seen, and Jackie was valiantly fighting off the vigorous advances of a squadron commander. I'd settled into a comfortable although slurred conversation with the Unitarian chaplain about the need to shun and reject the rigid dogma of other faiths. I promised I would, and that made him happy.

"Be a free spirit, Joni," he pleaded over the table as the band played *Love for Sale*.

"I will, I will."

"Color the book well."

"What? Color what book?" I asked.

"The coloring book. For religious liberals. I have one in my office. You can pick it up any time."

"I'll get over as soon as I can."

"Good. By the way, do you know any Congressmen?"

"No."

"I wish you did. I need support in the House."

The squadron commander insisted he take Jackie home. Finally, weary of fighting, she agreed, but only on condition that I accompany them. He reluctantly agreed, and we walked on either side of him. Occasionally he would sag and we'd prop him up by the elbows.

"Good night," we told him in front of the BOQ.

"Goo'night, sweet dreamers," he slobbered. Then he lurched forward in an attempt to kiss Jackie. She stepped aside, and he fell face first into the bushes by the side of the door. Jackie went to help him, but I grabbed her by the arm and led her into the BOQ.

"Let him sleep it off there," I counseled.

"But he'll catch cold, Joni."

"Don't be ridiculous. He's got enough antifreeze for Alaska in January."

Jackie reluctantly agreed, and we entered the BOQ. We expected to find a quiet, darkened building in which to indulge in a long and peaceful sleep. Instead, every light in the building was on, and girls were scurrying up and down the halls and in and out of rooms. They wore work clothes that ranged from dresses to slacks and sweaters, to bras and panties, and to just panties in Ginger's case.

"What's going on here?" I asked Marthas, who came walking past us with a bucket and mop.

"Ask my roommate," she grumbled, never breaking stride.

We walked farther up the hall and encountered Sarah Parsons.

"What is this, Sarah?"

"Cleanup. For inspection tomorrow." She looked around to make sure no one was listening, then said to us, "Look. Don't be mad at me like everybody else seems to be. Captain Alantean told me she was putting me in charge of the BOQ for inspection tomorrow. She told me that if we didn't pass, she'd have my head and everybody else's head. So I got everybody up and we're cleaning the place. So don't be mad, OK?"

"We have to clean it up *now?*" Jackie moaned.

"Right now. Inspection is at eight, and after all the things Box-Body told me had to be done, I don't think we'll make it working all night."

Jackie and I went to our rooms. "Don't lie down," I yelled as Jackie headed for the bed. "You'll never get up."

"I don't care. I don't care."

"You'll care tomorrow when they beat you for having dirt in your room."

"Do they really beat you, Joni?"

"How do I know? Come on and get changed. We'll pitch in fast and get it over with."

Sarah came in and told us what had to be done. Every inch of the room had to be scoured. The windows had to shine. The floor had to be scrubbed and waxed. The rugs had to be spotless. The globe on the overhead light was a favorite spot for the inspectors to check, so that had to be taken down and washed. All clothing in the closets had to be buttoned and hung neatly. Shoes were to be shined to a high gloss. All underwear in the drawers was to be rolled neatly. All other clothing was to be neatly arranged. Pictures had to be hung straight, and bathroom articles had to be clean and arranged in neat rows on clean shelves inside a spotless medicine cabinet.

"Make sure you clean out the insides of your suitcases," Sarah warned us. "Box-Body says they like to open them and gig you if they find any dirt inside."

"Is that like beating you?" Jackie asked.

"Gigging you? No. It's a point system. Get too many points and they punish you."

"*Then* they beat you."

"No, Jackie. They make you march or take away free time or something like that. Come on. Get with it. We're all going to meet at three and work together on the halls."

"On the halls?"

"Sure." Sarah was annoyed now. "The halls have to be done, too. Scrubbed and waxed. Same with the lobby." She cut short her instructions and left us in my room.

We eventually got with it, and after an hour our rooms were shaping up nicely. By two-forty-five we had everything completed except the floors, which we decided to tackle after the community project in the hall.

Outside the room, Sarah was in the process of organizing the work. Pails and mops were assigned, cleaning cloths handed out, and duties divided. We all went to work, but not before Sarah asked Ginger to put on at least a bra.

"It's too hot," Ginger protested.

"It's also disgusting," Sarah countered.

"Why, you jealous, miserable . . ."

"Shut up, you brainless mammary gland."

Jackie jumped in between them, suggested to Ginger that she wear a bra in case anyone entered the building, and cooled Sarah off by asking her to be tolerant of Ginger's shortcomings. I realized at that moment how effective a negotiator Jackie could be. I watched her mediate many fights from that day forward.

Actually, we didn't have to wait long before the next argument ensued. The phone rang in the hall just as I was cleaning it with a disinfectant.

"Hello," I answered.

"Hi there. Is Marthas there?"

"I think so. Who's calling?"

"Just tell her Ted."

I knew it was Ted Ruttish. I told him to hang on for a minute. Then I yelled up the hall, "Marthas. There's a man named Ted on the phone for you."

Marthas came running up the stairs and bumped into Ginger, who came out of her room.

"Ted's on the phone," Ginger snarled. "You kooky thief!"

Marthas looked her dead in the eye, screwed her face up into the hostility of a jungle cat, and hissed at Ginger. Her right hand went up like a cat's paw, fingernails extended for the kill. Her action truly frightened Ginger, who backed up a few steps. Marthas repeated the threat before continuing to the phone. She spoke in hushed tones—too hushed, unfortunately, for me to hear anything.

"That bitch," Ginger muttered as I passed her. Jackie was standing alongside her and again tried to calm things down.

"What are you mad about, Ginger?" she asked in a deliberately sweet voice. "You had a date with Harry tonight."

"Harry's a bum."

"No! I thought he was a partner."

"He tried to rape me."

We couldn't help laughing at the offhand way Ginger made the statement.

"You say he tried, Ginger? He didn't succeed?"

"I'm very selective about who I give myself to." She nodded her head to emphasize the point and flounced back into her room.

Jackie and I went back to our rooms and began working on the floors. We finished up at five-thirty and decided that the only way to be ready and present for the 8 A.M. inspection was not to go to bed at all. We showered, dried the walls of the shower with toilet paper, and slipped into clean cotton dresses.

"Let's go outside and get some air," I suggested.

The night air felt good, and we walked for almost an hour. We did a full circle and approached the BOQ from the rear. It was Jackie who first spotted the dark figure inching out of the second-floor window. We could see a man's shoes come through the window, then his legs, and finally the seat of his pants as he balanced on the windowsill on his stomach.

"Careful," a girl's voice said. "Careful."

"I'm trying to be," the man sputtered.

He inched farther out until he could no longer balance himself. His stomach slid across the sill, and he tried to kick himself out and away from the wall. He dropped into the bushes below with a heavy thud.

"Yaaaaaaaah," he yelled.

"Shut up," the girl said from the window above.

"I'm hurt," he protested.

She slammed the window shut.

We stood behind a tree and watched the man painfully get to his feet and fight his way out of the bushes. He limped away without our ever recognizing him. We looked up again at the window and tried to determine whose room it belonged to. But we weren't that familiar with the number of rooms and had to be content with narrowing it down between Sarah Parsons, Marthas Trouble, Ginger Whip, or her roommate, a chubby little girl named Barbara Thompson.

"We have some detective work to do tomorrow," I said to Jackie.

"Oh, we couldn't," she protested. "But I suppose it's our duty," she added. I nodded my agreement.

Chapter 9

"*The Weekend Is Free Except . . .*"

SHOWERS

WEEKEND DUTY

6 AM SAT. - INSPECTION
10 AM INFORMATION CENTER
4 PM CLOTHING CHECK
7 PM BRIEFING
• - SUNDAY -
6 AM CHURCH SERV.
4 PM GENERAL'S TEA
7 PM

The inspection team arrived promptly at 8 A.M. It was headed by none other than General Rufus Giddypate himself, a fact that sent Captain Alantean and Sergeant Morrose into alternating fits of glee and horror. Box-Body ran ahead of the team to make sure the next room to be inspected was ready. Alantean walked with the general and his aides and gave each girl stern looks to stave off any breach of military etiquette. We each stood at rigid attention while General Giddypate asked us senseless questions about our home towns and family and goals in life. As he did this in each room, his two aides were busy opening suitcases, running fingers over door moldings and Venetian blind slats, and pushing on beds to check on the tightness of the blankets.

General Giddypate was a seemingly pleasant man. He looked tough, his face wrinkled and tanned, his uniform a perfect fit over broad shoulders and a slightly paunchy midsection. He was the first general any of us had ever met face to face, unless, of course, Ginger had been engaged to one sometime back in her busy career. She didn't admit to this, however, after the inspection team had left the BOQ and we got together to compare notes.

All in all, we'd fared pretty well as a group. Jackie received two gigs for having some toothpaste residue around the cap of the tube. I received one gig for not buttoning the top button of my raincoat that hung in the closet. Marthas had the most trouble. One of the general's aides became quite upset over some of the paraphernalia in her closet. He was particularly mad about the piece of horsehair rope, a box full of Indian worry stones, amulets, and other charms, and another box containing the cloth, clay, and pieces of wood used by Marthas to make her little dolls.

"What is this piece of rope doing here?" the aide asked.

"It's one of the basic props of my religion, sir."

"What religion says you have to have a piece of—"

The general cut him off. "Freedom of religion is precious in the Air Force," he assured Marthas.

But the aide wasn't to be deterred.

"And what about this box of *junk?*" he pressed. "Is that part of your religion, too?" He was referring to the cloth and clay.

"No, sir," Marthas answered. "That's my hobby."

"Well, the regulations state that every closet . . ."

Again General Giddypate came to the rescue. "Hobbies are a valuable and worthwhile thing for every member of the Armed Forces. I have my own hobby, you know."

"What hobby is that, sir?" Marthas asked.

"Gardening. I love the outdoors, the mother earth, working with my hands. Keep your hobby, Lieutenant. Work hard at it and enjoy it."

"Yes, sir, I will." Marthas held back a small smile of triumph from the general's vision. But she let it come through for the flustered aide.

As soon as they left her room, she closed the door between it and Sarah's room, went to the window, and carefully hauled up three pieces of string. Attached to the end of each was one of the dolls she had in various stages of completion. She breathed a sigh of relief as she placed them back in her drawer, carefully covering them with a slip. She knew she'd have to be careful in the future. The aide had spent too much time inspecting the inside of the window, and a new hiding place would have to be found for future inspections. Besides, he would now be out to get her. Perhaps another doll . . . maybe later.

We climbed on the bus at 0900 for the base tour. It took the full two hours as Airman Kraus of the Information Office gave us a running commentary. Jackie and I slept most of the trip in our seats at the rear of the bus. We rolled back into the BOQ parking lot at eleven and happily piled out to begin what was left of our free weekend.

But Box-Body crushed that fleeting moment of eager expectation.

"The captain wants to see all of you now," she mumbled. "In the lobby."

We all moaned and griped. And we did as we were told. Alantean sat in the only overstuffed chair, a clipboard on her knee. When we gathered around her, each bearing our own individual expression of disappointment and apprehension, she broke into a large smile and told us all to sit on the floor.

"Well, girls, I know you've been looking forward to doing nothing for the next forty hours, and believe me, I've wanted that for you as much as you've wanted it." You can't really believe a statement like that, but you accept it. There's never any alternative.

"But there's been a change in plans around here that affects all of you—some more than others, but all of you. The first thing is General Giddypate's reception for new officers at the base. Remember the film on military etiquette? Well, the general has decided tomorrow would be a good day for the reception. And that means every one of you attends. Right?"

"Do we have to?" Penny Pross asked.

"Of course. It's not in the regs, but it's understood that every officer will attend. No question about it."

Alantean explained that the reception was to be held at one o'clock the following afternoon—Sunday.

"You don't have to stay more than an hour," she commented, evidently hoping to lessen the disappointment in the room. "But be there. And before you go, print your name and rank very neatly on these blank cards. When you get there, you put the card in the general's brass bowl on the little table next to the front door."

We all started to protest and argue, but Alantean cut all that short.

"Next," she went on, "has to do with the impression some of you made with Captain Penner, the IO. He wants to see the following names at his office tonight at five o'clock sharp. Moura, Sutherland, Whip, and Thompson."

"Not tonight," Jackie moaned. "Between the general's reception tomorrow and seeing Captain Penner tonight, that kills the whole weekend. Joni and I were planning to—"

"Lieutenant Sutherland," Alantean said with resignation, "I know it kills the weekend. And I am sorry. Please believe that. But you're in the Air Force now, and until you get through this basic training, you don't make plans that are more important than the Air Force's plans. Just accept that and you'll have a hell of a lot easier time."

Of course we accepted it. It was made easier by the pleasant switch in Captain Alantean's approach to us. Sitting there, she became a nice and understanding human being, nothing like the bellowing, hard-nosed, steel-backed captain we came to hate out by the flagpole at 4 A.M. "Go along with it, girls," she told us as she got up and headed for the door. "Three weeks will fly by and you'll be over this bad period. You'll be regular officers in the Air Force, and that's not a bad life, believe me." We knew she was right. It was just difficult to accept at the moment.

Jackie and I had planned to sleep all Saturday afternoon, have dinner, and then head for town and maybe a movie. Of course, that was still possible, provided the five o'clock meeting with Captain Penner didn't last very long.

"I wonder why he wants to see us," Jackie mused as we undressed and got ready to head for our respective beds.

"Who knows, Jackie? I'd think he'd want to see Sybil Longjohn or whatever her name is."

"Longstreet."

"Right. Longstreet. She seemed to be as well-read as he was. They had something in common, I thought."

"Maybe that's the problem. I think he's kind of phony, don't you?"

I was too tired to deliberate the question of Captain Penner's authenticity. But just as I was drifting off into a blessed sleep, I did think of the man we'd seen coming out of the window the night before.

"Hey, Jackie," I yelled.

There was no answer. She was already gone from the realities of being awake. I made a mental note to check with her when we got up concerning our investigation of which girl had entertained the mystery man in her room. General Giddypate's name was the last to pass through my mind before I went off to sleep. I remember giggling a little before all went black.

Chapter 10

"Join the Air Force and Become a Movie Star"

Barbara Thompson, Ginger's roommate, drove all of us over to Captain Penner's office. She was one of the few girls who'd brought a car to basic training, and it was a beauty, a long, sleek Buick with a stereo tape deck, power everything, and shag rugs throughout.

Barbara wasn't a talkative girl. But she was pleasant enough, although a bit sarcastic for my liking. There was a maturity about her seldom found in girls of our age, even though most of us were in our early twenties. She was a pretty girl, given to wearing heavy makeup and flashy clothes that didn't seem to look so heavy and flashy on her. On me, they would have looked like something out of a Tennessee Williams play.

Barbara drove as the rest of us speculated on the purpose of the meeting with Captain Penner. Ginger felt it might be for picture-taking. "I photograph very well," she said with a forced modesty, "and a man of Captain Penner's sensitivity and artistic achievements can sense that sort of thing."

Barbara glanced over at her roommate and smiled. Then she looked at us in the rear-view mirror and winked.

"Well, he did mention feature stories," I offered.

"Maybe it's just that he has a few more questions for the news release," was Jackie's evaluation.

"Maybe he wants to get laid!" Barbara threw that one in just as she was parking the car.

"Well, he certainly won't find *me* willin' to help him with that," Ginger answered her roommate. "I'm very selective about who . . ."

". . . rapes you." Barbara finished Ginger's thought and slammed the car door. There was no doubt this Barbara Thompson was a knowing girl, and a worldly one to boot. Jackie and I suddenly felt very freshmanlike in her sophisticated presence.

We entered the building and went to the information office. We entered the large outer office containing six or seven desks and a number of file cabinets. From where we stood just inside the door, we could see Captain Penner at his desk. He cast a quick glance at us as we entered, but didn't acknowledge we were there. Instead, he pretended not to have seen us and launched into a series of poses. He pulled his horn-rimmed glasses down on his nose and gazed intently at the paper in his typewriter. Then he looked up at the ceiling and started talking to someone up there.

"Leaving you is not the act of simplicity it may seem, Marsha. If you only knew the depth of emotion I face because of this act." His hand gestured at the ceiling before he looked back at his typewriter. He then reached for a shot glass on the desk and downed its contents—a musty brown liquid we assumed was bourbon or some other whiskey. He sat staring at the typewriter for a few moments and then slammed his hands down on the keys.

"Damn!" he exploded. He swung his chair around so that he faced the desk—and us.

"Oh, hi there. Come on in."

Penner got up to greet us. He was wearing a tan cotton shirt open at the neck. Over that was an expensive cardigan sweater in a deep rust color. His pants were baggy corduroy slacks.

"Hope you'll excuse my civilian garb. I like to be comfortable when I'm creating."

I knew he wanted to be asked what it was he was creating.

"Creating? What are you working on, sir?"

He seemed annoyed. "You would ask that."

I figured I guessed wrong.

"Oh, I'm sorry. I didn't mean to . . ."

"Well, that's natural, I suppose. Most people are interested in the latest work of a writer. It's a novel. A very broad work. I'm using a big canvas and working in broad strokes. It's contemporary. It's about man's inability to understand himself and his world."

"How psychological," Ginger exclaimed.

"Yes. Any good writer is a psychologist, you know. We must understand the human environment and mind."

We all nodded our understanding.

"Captain Alantean said you wanted to see us, sir," Jackie mentioned after Penner mumbled an apology for the shot glass on the desk. He said it was a curse of all serious writers, and we didn't quarrel.

"Yes. I didn't mention to you before that I'm also pretty well-known in film circles. I use my knowledge in filmmaking for the Air Force. We do a lot of films, you know."

"Yes. We've seen some of them."

"People don't realize it," Penner told us, "but we're actually doing many things cinematic that are ahead of the state of the art. Interesting, don't you think?"

Personally, I was getting tired of agreeing with Captain Penner. Jackie seemed to feel the same way, although Ginger appeared eager to hear more with which she could agree. Barbara just sat silently buffing her fingernails.

"Anyway, to make the proverbial long story shorter, we're

going to be producing a motion picture right here at the base. It's a sort of recruiting film for the Air Force Nurse Corps. And let me assure you we don't follow that silly Hollywood habit of using actors and actresses. We use the real people. Slice of life. Like it is. Avant garde. Up front."

"Are you tryin' to tell *me*, Captain Penner, that *I'm* goin' to be in a motion picture?" Ginger beamed.

"Well, that depends, Lieutenant. Or may I call you Ginger?"

"Oh, my, yes."

"Yes. You see, as the producer of the film, I've narrowed down the candidates for the starring role to the four of you." He took his glasses off, stuck one earpiece in his mouth, and swung around to look out the window.

"Just what is it we have to do?" Barbara asked, never looking up from her buffing job.

"Do?"

Barbara slowly shook her head back and forth for our benefit. "I assume we have to do something if we want to be in this movie you're talking about."

Penner swung back to face us and laughed. "You've read too many trashy Hollywood novels, Lieutenant. I suppose you were thinking I was going to turn this into a casting couch situation." He laughed again.

"I didn't think anything, Captain," Barbara said sharply. "You thought of the casting couch. If you don't mind, sir, I'm really not interested in making any movies. I'm a nurse, and I'm trying to become an Air Force nurse. I'm having enough trouble without making movies. I assume there's no extra pay involved."

"Of course not." Penner was riled. "This is a chance to do something worthwhile for your country. And besides, it gets you out of some of the routine for a few days."

Barbara got up from her chair. "Well, no offense, Captain, but I'd just as soon pass if it's all the same with you."

"Very well, Lieutenant Thompson. You're free to go. I should mention that I was also looking for girls to be on local radio and TV, pose for photos, and take part in a very special experimental program the Air Force is conducting with its new female officer trainees. I assume you're not interested in any of this."

"I suppose that's a correct assumption. Thank you for thinking of me, Captain." Barbara turned to us before leaving. "You girls don't mind if I cut out, do you?"

We assured her we didn't mind. After she left the office,

Captain Penner leaned across the desk. "Strange girl. Don't you agree?"

Jackie and I started to say we liked Barbara Thompson, but her roommate, Ginger, cut us off with, "I'm afraid I have to agree, Captain Penner. As her roommate, I confess I find Miss Thompson different from the kind of girl I'm accustomed to livin' with—if you know what I mean?"

"Let's just say I find her an interesting specimen as a writer. I once had a heroine in a novel very much like Miss Thompson. Perhaps we can talk about this sometime and help you to understand your roommate better."

"I'd certainly appreciate that, Captain Penner."

"Good. Now, let's get down to business. I do have this film to consider. And the local interview assignments. And, most important, this new Air Force experiment."

He went on to explain the new program. It seemed some high-ranking officer in Washington felt Air Force female officers weren't schooled properly in grooming and poise. He'd instituted a program in which new female officers would spend a week at one of the leading stewardess colleges in the country. The first girl to partake in the program was to come from our class.

We agreed it was interesting. Ginger seemed a little too excited, but that was to be expected. However, the movie project was obviously uppermost in her mind.

"Oh, my," she said as she fluttered her eyelashes at Penner, "I've never been in a real movie before. I was engaged once to a very famous director who told me I had a great deal of natural talent. Bless him. Do you really think *I* could do it, Captain Penner?"

"Of course, Ginger."

"Well, you certainly should know. I mean, a man of your artistic achievements. Don't y'all agree?" she asked us.

"By all means." Both Jackie and I knew Ginger would be in the movie. It didn't really bother us, although we both had to admit Ginger's all-out play for the assignment was a little annoying.

But Penner didn't want to seem too influenced by Ginger's game. He smiled at us and said he wanted to have some time to think about which one to choose.

"It might be helpful if I could talk privately with each of you before I come to a final decision. Would you all agree to that?"

We agreed.

"Fine. Would you stay this evening, Ginger? And I can talk with each of you after classes on Monday."

Further agreement.

Ginger and Penner decided they'd have a drink at the Officers' Club. We said we'd like to go into town, and Penner called a local taxi.

"You can wait right here in my office if you'd like until the cab comes," he told us. "Just snap the lights out."

He put things away in his desk before leaving, covered the typewriter, and left arm in arm with Ginger. We sat discussing Miss Whip for a few minutes as we killed time before the arrival of transportation. I started pacing the office, and it was while I stood at the window, keeping an eye out for the taxi, that I noticed the file folder lying on the radiator cover. Written on the little tab in Magic Marker was: *I Crave Your Body*. I picked it up and read the first paragraph of page one:

Richard peered through the blinds at the luscious redhead as she paraded naked before his leering eyes. He squeezed the handle of his whip with his sweaty right hand as his other hand . . .

"Jackie. Read this."

"You shouldn't be reading things like that, Joni. They might be top secret or something."

"I think this is top secret. For Penner. Come here."

Jackie sat in her chair and shook her head. "No, Joni. I will not read something that belongs to another person. I simply won't. *You* read it to me."

"I can't read it out loud. It's . . . It's . . . It's so dirty."

"Let me see." Jackie came over and looked over my shoulder at another page in the folder:

. . . the hunchback screamed with animal delight as he approached the mound of gold flesh lying so ready on the bed. He turned around and backed onto the bed, his hump a menacing but fascinating symbol to the exotic female so ready to accept . . .

"He's a pervert," Jackie gulped.

"He's a hunchback."

"Not him, Joni. Penner. Penner is a dirty-old-man pervert. He writes dirty-old-man perverted books. Some novelist he is."

I flipped through the remaining sixty pages. Each was studded with choice language and erotic descriptions of the sex act and variations upon the basic. And then I came to the letter:

Mr. Emmett Hays Berkley
c/o Captain Clarence Penner
111 Dunning Street

Dear Mr. Berkley:

Reference your latest book in the Bronze Medal series of adult titillation.

While we realize you've contributed seven books to this series, we do feel it necessary to extend some criticism to this, your latest work—I Crave Your Body.

We feel that you've perhaps slipped behind the times and are not currently abreast of the latest needs in erotic literature. It is no longer sufficient simply to portray a man and a woman together in the act of sex, no matter how explicit your descriptions may be. Today's market, more educated and aware of their times, demands and must be given honest situations with which they can more readily identify.

Homosexuality is definitely a must for all books in the series. Orgies must have no less than six characters actively participating in the games. Sadism, while perhaps distasteful to some of our writers, is fast becoming a popular form of social enjoyment and must be included in no less than seven scenes in this latest work under your pen name of Emmett Hays Berkley.

Might I suggest the use of a hunchback as a major character. It was the thought of the editorial board that a leper might fit handily into this new book of yours, but I convinced them you might have trouble handling that type of character. Perhaps in the next book.

There has also been criticism on the part of our editorial board toward the opening pages of your last two works. Consider Congressional Hooker. You spent a full two pages establishing Washington, D.C., as the scene. Obviously, the occasional book browser would not continue past the first page if he (or she) thought it was a book about our nation's capital. You must have a major sexual scene, sadistic if possible, on the very first page.

I also refer to the opening pages of Outer Space Mistress. While we were all in agreement that the very premise of the book was quite brilliant—loose woman on spaceship with astronauts—the use of two pages to set the scene for the launch was excessive. It would have been better if Peggy, the outer space mistress, had been in the act of some sex with astronaut Bruce Daring while he waited for the rockets to ignite. Do you follow our thinking? It all boils down to keeping up with the times. Our readers demand this, and so do your readers. Now that the name Emmett Hays Berkley is developing a loyal following, you must constantly work toward more imaginative perversions in every book you do for us.

I had some trouble convincing the publisher to give you that extra week you requested. He insisted on the usual three-week delivery of the manuscript, but he relented after I told him you'd need some research time on hunchbacks. Don't be a day late. He gets very nasty over late manuscripts.

All the best on your latest work. Enclosed is a check for $75.00 as one-half payment on the advance. The other $75.00 will be sent, as usual, after receipt and approval of your manuscript.

Yours sincerely,

Jonathan Greenleaf
Senior Editor
Vineyard Publishing, Inc.

"Can you imagine?" Jackie muttered.

"I knew there were those books, but I never knew anybody wrote them," I answered. "I mean anybody real that you might meet."

"Do you think we should tell Ginger?"

I pondered that for a moment as I carefully replaced the file folder on the radiator cover. "No, I don't think we should," I answered. "Ginger's worked very hard to get close to Captain Penner, and it wouldn't be fair to her. Besides, she was probably engaged once to a hunchback with a whip."

Our cab pulled up in front of the building and beeped his horn. We snapped out the lights, went down the hall and through the main entrance just as Captain Penner came to a screeching halt in his MG.

"Forgot something," he yelled as he ran through the door.

"We know," Jackie and I muttered.

Ginger was sitting in the MG. She waved and gave us a big smile. We returned it as we climbed into the cab.

" 'Bye," Ginger yelled.

" 'Bye," we responded. "And good luck."

We slept fairly late Sunday morning, attended church, had a light breakfast at the club, and got ready to attend the general's reception at his home. As one o'clock drew closer, we found ourselves becoming slightly excited. After all, it isn't every day that you attend an official reception at a general's home. At least it wasn't for us.

We carefully printed our names on the blank white cards, put on our best dresses, and climbed on the bus provided, as an afterthought, by Captain Alantean.

"We're going to park the bus a few blocks from the general's house," she told us after we'd climbed aboard. "And nobody mention the fact I got a bus to take you. Got that?"

"Yes, ma'am."

As we were pulling out of the parking lot, a long black Cadillac came into the lot and cut off the bus. Behind the wheel was Abraham Lefkowitz. Next to him was Harry. The back seat was filled with clothing boxes.

"The uniforms are here," Lefkowitz screamed at Alantean over the noise of the bus's motor.

"Leave 'em in the lobby," she replied.

"I can't do that," Lefkowitz said. "They'll all be stolen. I'll wait with them."

Alantean shrugged and told the bus driver to move on. Lefkowitz backed out of the way, and we headed for the Capehart Housing Development on the far west side of the base.

The bus stopped just at the beginning of the development, and we all walked together behind Captain Alantean.

"One more thing," she cautioned us as we approached what was obviously the largest house in the area. "Don't make it seem you all came in a group with me. The general wants to think each of you came because you wanted to. Don't spoil it for him."

We all walked through the front door together after being greeted by one of the general's aides, the same one who had conducted such a ruthless inspection of our rooms the day before. We'd started to follow him into the living room when Alantean stopped us with a hard look. She pointed to the brass bowl on the little table next to the front door. "Cards," she said in a stage whisper.

We all dropped our cards in the bowl. Well, all except Ginger, who'd forgotten hers. Captain Alantean scowled and continued to lead us into the living room, where General Giddypate stood talking with a number of young officers, mostly male.

"Moura," Alantean whispered to me, "you go first. Introduce yourself."

I stood frozen in a sudden seizure of fright.

"Go on," Alantean said again with an edge to her voice.

I tentatively approached the general and smiled.

"Well, hello there," he boomed, extending his hand to me. "Welcome."

"Thank you, sir. I'm Lieutenant Joni Moura. I'm a nurse."

"Ah, yes. I'm very proud of our nurse training program. Happy to have you aboard."

The rest of the girls followed my lead and went up to the general. He was extremely pleasant and soon had us laughing at his stories of the time he was in an Air Force hospital in Germany.

". . . and when that nurse tripped over my catheter, that was the last straw."

"Oh, my," Ginger twittered. "That must have smarted in the worst way, General."

"Only when I . . . I can't say it. Only when I laughed." Everyone roared.

The house soon became quite full, and General Giddypate suggested that some of us accompany him outside for a view of the Capehart project. We went with him onto his patio and surveyed what could be seen from there. We looked down over many homes that appeared to be just like any development community in suburban America. But one thing was different from what might be expected in a suburb in the heat of the dry Texas summer. Every inch of every lawn was a brilliant green. Everywhere the fine spray of water sprinklers cascaded into the air and caught the sun before coming to rest on the lush green ground.

"Everything's so green," Jackie said in admiration.

"You bet it is," General Giddypate said. "I insist on every blade of grass on this base being kept green and healthy. Just like my own garden."

We toured his garden, and it was lovely.

92

"All it takes is a little water," he told us as we walked back to his house and the refreshing air-conditioning. "A simple think like water to keep things green." We entered the house just as the general's aide came up to him.

"Sir. It's Mayor Bilkhauser on the phone."

General Giddypate's mood changed immediately. His face went sour, and he began mumbling to himself. "Excuse me," he said to us and stalked away toward the bedroom area. We decided it was time to leave, but Captain Alantean cautioned us against it. It wasn't proper to leave without officially saying good-bye to the general.

He returned a few minutes later and was no longer the jolly general. We bade him farewell, got back into the bus, and headed home to the BOQ.

"I guess the mayor and the general are good friends," I commented to Jackie on the way back.

"Not judging by his reaction to that telephone call," she answered. "He looked awful mad."

I asked Captain Alantean whether the base and the town got along nicely together.

"The base *is* the town," she replied. "But the town doesn't realize that. Why, if we left here, this town would dry up and blow away. But they're always bitching about something. They treat us like second-class citizens."

Mr. Lefkowitz was sitting in the lobby with Harry when we returned. They were surrounded by boxes, each containing a uniform. We excitedly sorted out the boxes and ran to our rooms to try them on. It was obvious that there was a strained relationship between Ginger and Harry, the partner. They didn't exchange a word, although Harry seemed ready to say something a couple of times.

"Love them, enjoy them," Mr. Lefkowitz bubbled at us as we left the lobby. "And remember one thing. It is also my privilege to represent, at below even wholesale cost, the finest line of civilian dresses in all the Southwest and beyond. Come see me. Satisfaction guaranteed."

No one was listening to him. We all slipped into our dress-whites and converged in the hall. Everyone seemed to have been refitted nicely. Ginger still suffered from too tight a skirt, but it wasn't as bad as the first fitting. There followed a lot of laughing and bad jokes, a few catty remarks about certain figures, some nonsense over Mr. Lefkowitz, and a great deal of random female chitchat. This moment seemed to mark the turning point in our brief military careers. It wasn't important that we didn't really know what lay ahead in our training. We all seemed to sense that the worst was over and that what was to come would be handled in our stride.

It was certainly cause for a party.

"Pizza and beer for everybody!" Jackie exclaimed.

The reaction was unanimous. We changed back into civilian clothing, piled into the few cars belonging to fellow students, and headed for town and a pizza parlor Jackie and I had seen last night. Ginger declined to join us, a date with persons unknown the reason. Her roommate, Barbara, also begged off, a headache her reason.

The pizza parlor was crowded, mostly with college kids from the nearby community college and airmen from the base. After we'd waited ten minutes or so, the owner pushed several tables together and we enjoyed the pizza and local beer.

A party of four middle-aged people at an adjacent table seemed to be enjoying our brand of merriment. One of the men, a pleasant-looking person, leaned over to Penny Pross and asked, "What's the party for? Celebrating a big exam or something over at the summer session?"

"Better than that," Jackie answered. "We're nurses at the base, and we just realized they aren't going to beat us for the next three weeks." She flashed a big smile at the man. He reacted by turning away from her and muttering to the other three people at his table.

"What'd you say to him?" I asked my roommate.

"Nothing, Joni. I just told him we're nurses at the base and . . ."

The man turned again to Jackie and said in quite a loud and angry voice, "Maybe you ought to nurse your general's sick head. That would be some worthwhile nursing." The four of them got up from their table, the man paid their check, and they left the restaurant. But before they departed, they had a few words with the owner of the place. He came over to us and shrugged his shoulders.

"Some mess your general has gotten things into," he told us. "Half my business is from the base and half is from the town. I serve the base and the town is mad. I don't serve the base and I go bankrupt. You should tell your General Gillyplatter or whatever his name is that he should shut off his water."

The owner left us our check and left us confused. As we paid the check on the way out, Penny Pross asked him directly what the fuss was about.

"Here." He handed her the Sunday newspaper. "If you're

94

going to live here, you ought to know about where you live."

We got outside and all peered over Penny's shoulder. There, in bold headlines, was the answer. MAYOR SLAMS GENERAL ON WATER WASTE, CALLS FOR CONGRESSIONAL PROBE

The story went on to outline the problem. It seems the water lines for the town ran directly through the Air Force base. Faced with the worst drought in fifty years, the town placed severe restrictions on all water use for its citizens.

But General Rufus Giddypate wouldn't cooperate. Despite frequent and ever-increasing demands that he also limit water usage on the base, the general refused to budge on his position. In fact, according to the reporter doing the story, General Giddypate issued an order requiring every unit and every resident of housing to increase the daily watering of shrubs and lawn areas.

"Cleanliness is of paramount importance to any military function," he was quoted as saying. "Taxpayer money has built this base, and God has given it trees and grass. Green will prevail. And so will clean trucks."

We drove back to the base debating both sides of the question. We agreed that the general was wrong and the townspeople were right. But knowing our thoughts on the subject really weren't of much importance, we quickly forgot about the problem and spent Sunday evening getting ready for Monday morning. This was to be our first day of actual classroom training in the art of military nursing, and we again began to feel the excitement of a new adventure. Of course, the new adventure would come only after the old adventure of getting up at 4 A.M. and building muscles. This realization put all of us to sleep in a minimum of time.

Chapter 11

"You Can Get Used to Anything"

The early-morning grind did become easier as the week wore on. Getting out of bed never seemed easier, but the physical act of exercise was not as shattering as before. Of course, all of us learned how to cheat a little. We learned how to lift our fannies off the ground during push-ups so that it looked like our whole body was lifted. The right rhythm during deep-knee-bends and toe-touches could cut in half the actual motions. We were becoming veterans in record time.

Monday, our first day of actual classes, was interesting and easy. We were greeted before the start of the first class by Captain Monoman. He was as nervous as the first time we'd met him. He completely avoided Marthas' attempts at communication, kept his eyes riveted to the floor as he gave his brief lecture on the general responsibilities of an Air Force nurse.

"Any questions?" he asked the floor.

Ginger raised her hand. Monoman didn't see her.

"Sir," she said.

"Yes?"

"May I make an appointment with you later today?"

Monoman cringed. He snuck a glance up to make sure it wasn't Marthas asking the question. Reassured a little when he realized it was only Ginger, he answered in the affirmative. It was after he'd agreed that he thought to ask why Ginger had made such a request.

"Wh-wh-why?"

"It's personal, sir."

"Ooooh." Monoman sounded very weak.

Marthas fumed in her seat as Ginger turned to her and said, "All's fair, Marthas, in love and combat."

"Om," Marthas whispered at Ginger. "Om."

"You'd better watch out, Ginger," Barbara Thompson told her as we left class. "Marthas is liable to put a curse on you for eternity."

"Fat chance," Ginger snickered.

Jackie and I sat together during lunch after the morning round of classes that included basic Air Force hospital administration, procedure, and programs. It was at lunch that we made a mental list of unresolved questions concerning our classmates and some of the officers we'd come to know in the past few days.

First, there was the obvious—Marthas Trouble. Just how crazy was she? She could be so nice and normal, but she always reverted to the superstitious thing.

And then came Captain Monoman, obviously hung up by the same beliefs as Marthas.

Ginger Whip. Why did she want to see Monoman after class?

Captain Ted Ruttish. What did he see in Marthas?

Who was the man coming out of the BOQ window at six in the morning?

Was Captain Penner as perverted as his writing indicated? Would Ginger become the model of his newest work?

And would Congress come here to the base and strip General Giddypate of his rank before the entire base?

Jackie seemed reluctant to pursue any course that would help answer some of these questions. She reminded me of the virtue of minding one's own business. She referred to recent wire-tapping debates. And she quoted me the Bible. "Do unto others as you would have them do unto you," she said.

"What's that got to do with it?" I snapped. "I don't climb out of men's windows at six in the morning, do I?"

"That's not the point, Joni. It's a matter of—"

"Look, Jackie," I interrupted. "Let me handle the way we find out about these things. Don't tell me you haven't got a little curiosity about them."

Jackie agreed that she was humanly curious. And I agreed to use the maximum of tact and taste in my quest for the answers.

"I promise no one will know we're prying," I told my roommate.

"Then it's all right," Jackie said.

I started the investigation that night at the club. Jackie and I were at the bar with a group of students when I spotted Ted Ruttish hobble through the leather doors and approach the bar.

"Jackie. Look," I whispered.

Ruttish came over to us. His right leg was encased in a cast up to the knee. His face was scratched, and every movement seemed to pain him. He kept placing his hand on his stomach and groaning a little. Jackie shot me a tight-lipped stare to remind me of my promise to be discreet and tasteful.

"Hi, Ted," I chirped. "Fall out of a window or something?"

"Oh, my God," Jackie moaned, burying her face in her hands on the bar.

Ruttish reacted just as I thought he would. He gulped, turned white, and excused himself. He stumbled toward the

99

rest rooms, catching a few elbows in his stomach on the way through.

"Well!" I said to Jackie with a smug confidence. "It was Captain Ted Ruttish we saw. What do you think of that?"

"I'm humiliated. That's what I think of that. Besides, the simple fact that he's wearing a cast and has scratches on his face and an obviously sore belly doesn't prove he was the one. That's circumstantial evidence."

"Yes. And the circumstance is that he climbed out of . . . whose window? We don't know that, do we?"

"No, we don't, Joni. And we don't know Ted was the man."

"I'm satisfied it's Ted. And I can find out whose window it was."

"Well, just leave me out of it," Jackie said with resolution. We sipped our drinks in silence until we saw Ruttish heading back to the bar. Then Jackie turned to me and said quickly, "OK. So it was Ruttish. Just don't be so heavy-handed when you find out about the window. OK?"

"Right." Her change of heart was a booster to my enthusiasm. I was ready to probe further. But Ted dashed my hopes as he detoured from his course to us and headed for Marthas Trouble who'd just entered the bar area. He hobbled up to her, took her by the arm, and led her to a small table at the far end of the room.

"Damn," I muttered.

"You'll just have to wait to find out, Joni."

"Oh, no," I answered, still watching Ruttish and Marthas. "I know it was Marthas' window. I just wanted to get it from Ruttish himself."

"How do you know?"

"I counted the windows the next day, silly. He came out of Marthas' room."

"Why didn't I think of that? And why didn't you tell me?"

"Oh, I figured you wouldn't believe me. Besides, it would have been fun to hear Ruttish admit it."

"Isn't that something?" Jackie mused. "Captain Ruttish and Lieutenant Trouble. I'd never have dreamed."

I reminded Jackie that Ruttish and Marthas had been pretty cozy at the club on Friday night. Of course, we'd all felt it was just because Ginger had shown up with Harry, the partner. We'd never dreamed Marthas would allow Ruttish into her room and . . . well, what *could* they be doing in the room at that hour? I asked Barbara Thompson what she thought, careful never to mention any names or specifics.

"Barbara, if you caught a man sneaking out of one of our BOQ windows at six in the morning, what would you assume he and the girl in the room were doing?"

"Getting laid," she said flatly. "Who're you talking about? Ruttish and Trouble?"

"You know," Jackie and I said in unison.

"Sure. My room's next to the kook's room. I guess they don't oil the beds we have, 'cause it squeaked like hell that morning."

"How did you know it was Ruttish?" Jackie asked.

"Because she kept moaning, 'Ted—Ted.' Who else could it be?"

Jackie and I ate dinner in an embarrassed silence. Marthas and Ruttish left together about seven. Ginger and Captain Penner showed up for a drink and left soon after. We gloomily finished our meal and went back to the BOQ.

"Well, I hope you're satisfied, Joni," Jackie scolded as she got ready for bed. "I hope you've learned your lesson about snooping."

"Yes, I have, Jackie. It's all pretty silly, I guess."

We didn't exchange another word until just before turning off the lights.

"Joni?" Jackie said as she stood in the bathroom doorway.

"Yes, Jackie?"

"Do you think Marthas is attractive?"

"I guess so, in her own way."

"Well, what I mean is, what do you think Ted Ruttish sees in her?"

I was about to throw some of Jackie's words back at her, but that would have been nasty. Besides, I was tickled she still had interest.

"I don't know what he sees in her. Maybe he wants her to cast a spell over his superior."

"Or over Ginger, maybe. Did you ever think of *that?*"

I hadn't thought of that possibility. And I fell asleep developing that theory to its fullest conclusion.

Chapter 12

"Roll 'em!"

Ginger was chosen to star in the recruiting film under Captain Penner's guiding hand. To our surprise, Jackie and I were also chosen to be in the film in smaller roles. It was all very exciting; the only damper was Captain Alantean's obvious disagreement as to what a student nurse should be doing during her three-week training period.

"If you wanted to be in movies," she told us, "you should have gone to Hollywood instead of in the Air Force."

We told her we hadn't asked for the assignment, but her mind was made up. We were goldbrickers, as far as she was concerned, and if she had her way, Captain Penner and the whole information organization of the Air Force would be sent to Vietnam with rifles and helmets.

So, under this cloud of protest, Ginger, Jackie, and I reported to Captain Penner's office at 7 A.M. the following Thursday morning. We'd hoped to be excused from calisthenics, but Captain Alantean wouldn't hear of it. We ran our laps, did our exercises, showered, had breakfast, and showed up at Penner's office exhausted.

He introduced us to the film's producer-director. His name was Slate Hardman. He was very big and very fat and sported a full beard and very long hair.

"What a great pleasure," Ginger cooed. "I've certainly enjoyed your films, Mr. Hardman."

Hardman looked shocked. "You have?" he asked with disbelief.

"Oh, yes. I'm sure I've seen them all," Ginger continued. "I understand you certainly are one of the more creative geniuses in Hollywood."

"Hollywood? Yes."

"Do you live there all the time," Ginger asked, "or do you spend a lot of time on the Continent?"

"Yes. Ah, Milwaukee is my home and base of operation. I avoid that Hollywood trap whenever possible."

"Oh, I understand, Mr. Hardman. Wicked ol' Hollywood corruptin' one's true talent."

"Yes. That's exactly it." Hardman looked to Penner for some support. Penner just smiled and handed us the scripts for the film.

The covering page contained the title: AIR FORCE NURSE—OFFICIAL USAF FILM X7-19YB.

"How original," Ginger exclaimed.

We were told to read through the script while Slate (he asked us to be informal with him) and Captain Penner went out to check on the crew and the first setup. We sat studying the script in silence. It seemed to be nothing more than a series of little scenes in which nurses were shown performing the routine duties of our trade. There were no lines to be spoken; the only sound indicated by the script was that of a narrator and some music.

"I don't understand," Ginger said to us. "I was led to believe I'd be sayin' a lot in the movie. That's what Captain Penner told me. He said he thought I had one of the most interesting ways of speakin' he'd ever heard in all his career as a writer and film-maker. I don't see anything here where I speak. Do you see anything?"

"I don't see anything in this script, Ginger," Jackie answered. "Maybe he meant when they make movies out of his novels."

She perked right up. "Of course. Dumb me. I'm sure that's just what he meant. Besides, he also told me I had a very expressive face. He said I'd make an excellent me-me."

"Didn't he mean mime, Ginger?"

"Well, whatever. Oh, my, aren't y'all excited about bein' in a movie?"

We started to answer, but Ginger's heart and soul prompted her to add, "Now don't y'all go gettin' discouraged. After all, you may have a small part in this movie, but we all have to start somewhere, now don't we?"

What can you say to a girl like Ginger? We just nodded and secretly wished we were back with the others in class.

Slate Hardman returned half an hour later and informed us they were ready to shoot the first scene. According to the script, it was the scene in which the three of us would be photographed entering the base hospital. The instructions were to enter the picture from across the street, wave a friendly hello to some passing doctors, climb the steps, and walk briskly through the hospital's main entrance doors. It all seemed easy enough.

At the hospital a small flurry of activity was taking place on the sidewalk in front. Two young men, no older than in their late teens, stood arguing. They both looked like carbon copies of Slate Hardman, younger and their fat a little more firm, but replicas nonetheless.

"He said *I* could run the camera," one of the boys yelled at the other.

"He did not," the other protested. He spotted Slate approaching with us and ran up to his elder look-alike.

"You said I could take the pictures, Pop," he whined.

Hardman got very upset. He grabbed the boy by the arm and yanked him away from us.

"I told you not to call me Pop, damn it . . ." We couldn't hear the rest of it. It seemed kind of silly to try to hide the fact that they were father and sons. It was pretty obvious, and, anyway, a father should have pride in his sons. Mr. Hardman belted the son behind the ear as they reached the other son. There was another angry exchange of words as the other son backed into the tripod, sending the big camera falling into the arms of Captain Penner.

"I don't think things are going very well," I said.

"You just don't understand these show people," Ginger corrected me. "They're very temperamental."

"Oh."

"Try to understand, Joni."

"I've been trying since we got here, Ginger."

She didn't respond. She just set off in her sexiest walk toward the squabbling people around the camera.

"Y'all stop fightin', you hear?" she told them. "I'm ready to start the filmin'." Hardman's sons stood with their mouths open, their eyes boring holes through Ginger's uniform blouse.

"That's the spirit, Ginger," Captain Penner said proudly. "We've got to remember the budget. Is your crew ready to go, Slate?" he asked.

Slate looked at his two sons, who were still trying to undress Ginger.

"They're ready," he said, his voice directed to them.

"It's amazing, Slate," Penner told him as they walked to the front steps of the hospital, "how much alike your crew looks and how much they resemble you."

Slate shrugged his shoulders. "I guess it's because we've worked so closely for so long. Besides, the beards have a lot to do with that."

"That's for sure, Slate. I'd have a beard myself if it weren't for the regs. Very creative, a beard."

"Yeah." Hardman stopped just outside the hospital doors, looked back to where his sons stood with the camera, and yelled, "Let's make a movie."

"He talks so good," Ginger giggled as she indicated to one of the sons that she was ready.

"I got a little proposition I wanna talk to you about later," he replied. "OK?"

"It sounds very secret," Ginger replied.

"Yeah, it is. I think you'll like it, though."

Slate came back and briefed us on how and where to walk. We ran through it once, came back, primped a little, and waited for his cue, which, he said, would be "Action!"

One son stood behind the camera while the other held the hinged board in front of the camera. It had written on it in grease pencil: Nurse Film—Scene 1—Take 1.

"What's that thing?" Ginger asked the son behind the camera.

"It's called a slate."

"Oh, my, what an honor for Mr. Hardman to have that named after him."

The son looked at her with admiration. "Yeah. Don't forget later."

"OK," Hardman yelled, "walk!"

No one moved.

"Come on, come on," he snapped. "Let's go."

"Is this action?" I asked.

Hardman snapped his fingers. "Oh, yeah. OK, girls. Action!"

We started to walk. Hardman asked his son behind the camera, "How's it look, Clyde?"

"Looks great. When do you wanna start shooting?"

"STOP!" Hardman yelled at us. He turned to his son and began screaming abuses at him.

"You didn't say to start the camera," his son protested.

"So I didn't. So use your head, damn it. Let's do it again."

We came back to our starting positions and waited for Hardman's cue.

"All right," he said. "Roll camera. ACTION!"

We started our walk again. We were halfway there when Ginger suddenly stopped, turned until she was half-facing the camera, looked up to the sky, and said, "My, what a lovely day to be an Air Force nurse."

"CUT!" Hardman roared. "What the hell are you doing?"

"I was ad-libbin'," Ginger yelled back with a smile. "I thought it was of more interest to be doin' somethin' than just walkin'."

"Well, I don't think it is," Hardman exploded. "If I want some stupid broad telling me what . . ."

Captain Penner jumped in and cut Hardman off.

"Easy, Slate, easy. She's a very sensitive girl. Besides, I've got a little thing going with her, you know?" He gave Hardman a big, broad wink and a leer.

Hardman gave Penner a gruff laugh. "Nice stuff," he mumbled. "I'll try to take it easy with her. But *I* can't have a lot of screw-ups. Not with this budget."

Hardman was very polite as he asked *us* merely to walk straight as the script called for. The two young doctors were waiting inside the building to come out just as we approached the steps. Ginger pouted a few moments, but Penner put his arm around her and whispered in her ear.

"Oh, all right," she said.

We did the walk again. We almost made the steps, but Jackie got a pebble in her shoe and started hobbling.

"At twenty cents a foot for stock I'm already losing money," Hardman snarled at Penner.

We did it again, only this time Ginger threw a kiss to one of the young male doctors as they came out of the hospital on cue.

Hardman was really boiling now.

"One more take, Slate baby, and we'll be golden." To appease Hardman, Penner had lapsed into what he considered Hollywood dialogue.

We made it on the fourth take, to the relief of everyone concerned.

"Now we shoot the inserts," Hardman barked.

We asked what inserts were. He explained that once the master scene was photographed—in this case the one of us walking—he'd now take more footage of us from the front, close-ups, and other angles.

"Bring the camera up on the steps," he told his number one son.

"I'm hungry," was the answer. "Let's eat and then do some more."

"It's only nine-thirty," Hardman answered. "We eat at noon. That's what the union says."

The son who'd suggested eating beckoned to his father with a finger. Slate went to the son. The son whispered in his ear. Slate returned to Captain Penner and, in a hearty and joyous voice, announced, "Let's take a break for a second breakfast. He reminded me I need the time to plan the next scene."

Penner didn't like the idea but said nothing. We all went to the Officers' Club, had coffee and stale Danish rolls, and sat until the hungry son decided he was ready to resume.

I casually mentioned to him as we walked back to the hospital that I was surprised Mr. Hardman had agreed to take a break so soon. The son snickered and said, "What's so surprising? If the Air Force knew my old man brought his kids along as his crew, they'd cancel his contract. When he bid the job, he said he'd bring a full union crew. He never does, though. That's how he gets all these cheapie jobs."

I felt very in-the-know from that point forward. When I mentioned it to Jackie, her first reaction was that we should inform Captain Penner immediately. "After all, Joni," she said, "it's our tax money that's paying for the movie. The Air Force should know."

But we didn't tell anyone, although there were times during the day that we almost slipped in front of Captain Penner. And Penner himself had become suspicious.

"Do you know anything about those two fellows in the crew?" he asked us late that afternoon.

"No, sir. Just that their names are Clyde and Horace."

"I can't believe they're not related, can you?"

"I guess they've worked together too long, Captain." He seemed satisfied with that.

By the end of the day we'd managed to accomplish what seemed to us to be very little. We didn't leave the steps of the hospital until noon. Lunch took two hours, most of which was taken up by Captain Penner's sales pitch to Slate Hardman.

"I tell you, Slate baby, some of the books I've written are naturals for filming. I tell it like it is, you know. Raw guts. Emotions. And that's what the people want today. Truth. Honesty."

"Sex," Hardman added, wiping lemon sherbet from his beard.

"You bet," Penner concurred. "I write good sex, Slate. You ought to read some of my properties."

It was obvious Slate Hardman really wasn't interested in Penner's writings. But he was aware of his seller-buyer relationship with the captain and grumbled he'd read something that evening. That small word of encouragement was enough to lift Penner into a stratosphere of bliss. He slapped Hardman on the back, loudly told him what a fine crew he'd assembled for the nurse recruiting film, and led him out of the dining room like the manager of a newly crowned world boxing champion. Hardman's sons, Clyde and Horace, dragged along behind, each trying for position over Ginger's shoulders for a better look down her blouse front.

We spent the afternoon photographing around the exterior of the hospital and other buildings on the base.

"We've got good sun," Hardman told Penner. "We'll do the interiors tomorrow."

We were photographed entering and exiting our BOQ,

entering and exiting the Officers' Club, entering and exiting the Base Exchange store, entering and exiting the laundry, the bookstore, base headquarters, the motor pool, the commissary, and Abraham Lefkowitz's Uniforms of Paris emporium. Mr. Lefkowitz insisted he should be in the picture waving good-bye to us as we left the store. Hardman wanted no part of this, but Captain Penner urged him to include a shot of Lefkowitz.

"He's very close to General Giddypate," Penner told Hardman. "We'd better use him. Good PR, Slate baby."

So Abraham Lefkowitz stood at the door and grinned while we admired one another's uniforms as we came through the door.

We stopped work at five and all went to the club as guests of Captain Penner. One of the two sons—I think it was Horace—expounded at the bar on how wrong all war was for mankind. Naturally, he caught the attention of the officers at the bar who, after some kind and tentative arguing of the point, became irate and even approached violence toward the bearded son of a film-maker.

Slate Hardman took Horace to the men's room and, I assume, straightened out his tongue, at least for the duration of their stay around military people. They came back to the bar, and Horace sat silently staring down the officers with whom he had argued.

Clyde sat next to Ginger at the bar. He was annoyed that we were there at all. He kept trying to get Ginger to leave with him, but she remained coy and noncommitted.

Finally, after the third round of drinks, she told us she'd accepted the invitation to have dinner with Hardman's number one son.

"Sir," she slurred at Slate, "I've accepted your son's invitation to join him for dinner."

"Son?" Penner indignantly asked. "He's your son?"

Hardman started to sweat under his beard and hair.

"Yes," he muttered. "Both my sons. And worthless, too."

Penner looked around to see if anyone had overheard the exchange. Confident that no one was making an attempt to listen, he leaned close to Hardman and said, "I have a copy of your bid and contract with me, Slate. It forbids the use of family in producing Air Force films. You stated in your bid that you would use only top professional union talent."

Hardman sighed deeply and ordered a refill on the drinks. He turned to Penner, smiled, and said, "What do you care about unions? Look, you and I are in the same business.

We're both creative. Me? I'm in a rut making these damn movies for the government. You think I like making this trash? You think I like bidding so low I have to bring these two idiots along with me? You bet I don't. You? You're obviously a man of great creative literary ability. But you're in *this* rut." He waved his hand at the officers at the bar. "So let's you and me get together. Maybe I'll take one of your books and break out with it. How's that sound?"

Penner scowled, mostly to give himself time to check our reactions and to give himself time to think.

"My goodness," Ginger said as she got off her bar stool, "I never dreamed I'd cause such a fuss. I believe I'll just go to dinner with this nice boy and let y'all fuss alone."

Jackie and I decided it was time for us to vacate also. We excused ourselves, assured them we'd be back at Captain Penner's office bright and early the next morning. Ginger came with us to the ladies' room before going on with Clyde. Inside the rest room she bubbled over with excitement.

"I'm goin' to have a screen test tonight."

We both looked at her in what was probably an expression of profound puzzlement.

"A screen test, sillies," she continued. "Clyde, Mr. Hardman's son, feels I have talent that could be . . . what was it he said? . . . oh, yes, exploited . . . that's what he said. And he knows some people in New York who are lookin' for new talent. Isn't that excitin'? He's gonna take some pictures a me back at the motel and ship 'em right off to New York. I'm so excited I don't know if I can perform like I should."

Jackie seemed pained and concerned. After taking a quick peek to insure no one was in the rest room with us, she turned to Ginger in a very motherly manner and said, "Ginger, I like you. We all like you down deep. Do you want to be an actress or a nurse?"

"Oh, silly," Ginger said, shaking her head. "Bein' a nurse is just fine for somethin' to do for a while. But I've always had actin' in my blood. And anyone would be a fool to pass up an opportunity like this. Don't y'all agree?"

Jackie seemed even more pained and concerned. "But, Ginger, how do you know this Clyde . . . this beard . . . really can do something for you? I mean, after all, why not talk to his father? He's the one seems to know something about movie-making."

" 'Cause his daddy's an ol' fool. That's what Clyde said. His daddy just makes these silly little movies for the Air Force and like that. But Clyde is soon gonna begin makin'

111

real Hollywood movies. With his friends in New York. He's the one who's really gonna be somethin' someday."

Jackie gave up. We wished our fellow student well, left the club, and went back to the BOQ. What occurred that night at the motel could only be pieced together from the various stories of Ginger, Clyde, Horace, Penner, and Slate Hardman. But evidently what happened was that Clyde took Ginger for a cheap dinner in a local greasy spoon and rushed her back to the motel. He took her to his room where the camera was set up and locked the door.

"OK," he said as soon as the lock was turned, "let's get started. You can undress in the bathroom."

Ginger stood up in her tallest and most indignant pose and answered, "Undress? I'm certainly not one of those kind of girls."

Clyde threw his hands into the air and did a fast walk around the room. "What kind of girl?" he asked as he paced. "What kind of girl is Jane Fonda? What kind of girl is Susan Strasberg? What kind of girl was Marilyn Monroe? And how about Julie Andrews?"

"Julie Andrews?" Ginger retaliated. "Mary Poppins? What has she got to do with undressin'?"

"I'll tell you what she's got to do," Clyde said. "Even Mary Poppins is going nude. If you kept up with the biz, you'd know that. That's right. Even Julie Andrews is doing a nude scene in a film. That's it, baby. All the taboos are over. The body is beautiful. Everybody's got one. And if you wanna make it in movies today, you show the body. Only you show it artistic. I'm an artist. You'll love your body when you see what I do with it."

"Well, I already love my bo . . . Oh, I'm all confused. I do know films are much more liberal than they ever were before. Only you must understand I'm a very modest girl and . . ."

"Yeah. I know. Look, Ginger, my backers in New York are pushing me every day to come up with a new star. It could be you. But I've got to have test shots to . . ."

Ginger was already in the bathroom and undressing. When she was down to her bra and panties, she looked at herself in the mirror. "It's different when it's for an artist," she told her mirror image. She unsnapped the bra and slipped out of the panties. She looked at herself again. "At least he's not just another grabbin' fella. At least he's an artist." She grabbed one of the motel towels and wrapped it around her. She

112

struck a last pose in front of the mirror, pouted her lips, and opened the door leading to the bedroom. She took one step across the threshold and let out a shriek as Clyde's hand shot out from where he was hiding along the wall and grasped one of Ginger's breasts. Her hand went up in the air and the towel dropped to the floor.

"How dare you, you . . . you . . . you . . ."

"Relax," Clyde said with a grin. "You seemed tense, and I don't want that to come through on the test. Just thought I'd loosen you up a bit."

"Well, you certainly did that," Ginger said in a scolding voice. She picked up the towel and wrapped it around her again. "I don't need to be *that* loosened up."

Ginger sat on the couch while Clyde fiddled with the 16-millimeter camera on the tripod. He set up two bright lights that illuminated the couch and nodded to Ginger that he was ready.

"OK," he said. "First, let me get some face shots. Animate. Smile and cry and look mad and look sad."

Ginger did all those things as best she could. Clyde kept encouraging her with shouts of, "Beautiful. Yeah, yeah. Groovy. Too much, baby." All these words of praise, mixed with the liquor Ginger had consumed earlier, led her on to greater heights of emotion. She screwed up her face and tucked up her knees and really went to town on what she considered a prima performance. Of course, Ginger had no way of knowing that Clyde had widened the angle on the camera's zoom lens and was now taking in the entire length and width of the couch. The camera rolled on, the 400-foot film magazine churning away while Clyde stood smirking at the scene before him.

Ginger jumped up on all fours and purred like a kitten at the lens. She covered her bosom with her hand and adopted a shocked expression on her face. She winked at the camera. She ran a hand suggestively up one leg. She grabbed the telephone and used it as a prop in various poses. Ginger was "on," much to Clyde's delight.

Clyde didn't interfere at all. He just let the scene unfold until the change in sound of the film magazine indicated the 400 feet had run through.

"Take a breather, honey," he told Ginger as he changed magazines.

"My, my," she gasped, "actin' is a lot harder work than people assume, isn't it?"

"Yeah, yeah." Magazine changed, Clyde put Ginger back to work. This time he posed her on the bed.

After running through that 400 feet of film, he changed magazines again, shifted the camera and lights to the bathroom, and had Ginger go through various antics with the shower curtain as a prop.

Finally, with a fourth 400-foot roll of film on the camera, Clyde suggested that Ginger pretend a monster had come through the door and was after her. To insure uniform lighting all over the room, he put into use every light in the case. Soon the room was lighted up to a brilliant intensity.

"I'll tell you what," he said. "I'll use an extreme wide-angle lens and let it roll. I'll be the Monster and chase you around the room. It'll be more true to life."

"Oh, my. Well, all right. But no touchin', hea'?"

"I hea', baby."

Clyde flipped the switch and the camera started rolling. He crouched in a menacing pose and slowly stalked Ginger. She shrieked and jumped around and went from corner to corner.

"Yeah, baby, yeah," Clyde gulped. "What a star you're gonna be."

While this fourth reel of cinematic history was being filmed, Captain Penner and Slate Hardman roared into the motel parking lot in Penner's MG. They were both gooned. Penner climbed out of the car and beat his chest as he looked up to the heavens.

"Freedom, freedom in my bones," he chanted. "No more damn blue uniforms."

"That's the spirit," Hardman mumbled as he fell out of the MG face first, his beard kicking up some Texas dust.

"Oh, I almost forgot," Penner announced as he stumbled back to the car and reached inside. He pulled out seven leather-bound editions of his literary output.

"Leather," he told Hardman as they fell against each other. "Only the best for you, Slate baby, baby."

They staggered toward the motel entrance arm in arm.

"You're gonna love my books," Penner said.

"You bet your ass I will," Hardman said, belching over the line.

It was Hardman who noticed the window as they approached the motel entrance. He didn't say anything as he stopped abruptly, clutched his throat, and let out a violent gurgle. Penner then saw the window and vibrated his head to clear up his alcoholic vision. And then Hardman heard the cough from the bushes across the parking lot. He looked over. At least a dozen pair of eyes were visible in the neon glow of the motel sign. The eyes could be seen peering over and through the foliage. One pair of eyes blazed from the limbs of a young tree.

The object of all this attention was, of course, Clyde's motel window. The Venetian blinds were pulled in such a way that the interior of the room was visible through the slats. Although closed by Clyde, they'd stuck half open to form a horizontal grid that did little to protect those inside the room. The blazing lights spilled out through the blinds like the lights on a stage.

On-stage were Ginger and Clyde. Clyde had donned a big rubber nose and glasses and had Ginger trapped in a corner of the room.

"Roaaaaaaaaaar," Clyde went.

"Away, dirty old beast," Ginger responded.

Clyde was about to pounce on his prey when Slate Hardman rushed the window. He leaped off the ground, sending his huge frame crashing against the wall just under the window. His arm went straight through the lower pane of glass and he bellowed, "Roaaaaaaaaaaaar." Ginger screamed and Clyde flattened against the wall, his hands ready in the classic judo defense position.

"I was supposed to get her," Penner mumbled over and over to himself as he fought to hold back the tears.

Clyde finally tore himself away from the wall and attacked the window. He poked his head out and looked down at his father, who lay in a heap.

"Jeez, Pop," Clyde said in an annoyed whine. "Jeez."

Ginger got dressed in the bathroom, then sat pouting on the couch, a cigarette nervously dangling from her mouth. Penner got Slate Hardman up and into his son's room, where, after discovering Clyde had used up 1600 feet of color film, Slate threw another tantrum and proceeded to put his hamhock fist through the wall. Captain Penner launched into a long dissertation to Ginger on how she'd disgraced the United States Air Force.

"And it's all your fault," she told Penner.

"It is not my fault." He'd launched into another speech when Horace, number two son, came down the hall, a mousy little blonde on his arm and a wide grin on his face. He knocked on Clyde's door and Slate opened it. The sight of his father threw Horace into a momentary dither.

"Oh, hi, Pop. This here's Matilda. I was going to shoot some footage of her and—"

"You must be the famous Slate Hardman," the little mouse squealed. "Horace has told me all about you. I certainly do appreciate your helping me be in the movies."

"Roaaaaaaaaaar," Slate growled.

And the motel owner came down the hall and told them to shut up or he'd have them all thrown in jail.

"And tell your water-hogging general that, too," he added as he slammed the door and headed back to the office.

The next morning was tense. Slate Hardman talked to no one. He'd had to place a call to Mrs. Hardman in the middle of the night, telling her to ship more film to him the first thing in the morning. Presumably it was on the way.

Horace and Clyde were still arguing over Clyde's having used all the film and leaving none for Horace and Matilda.

Ginger went to sick call and spent the day in her room.

And Captain Penner assigned Airman Kraus to be with the film crew while he attended to more pressing business. It was obvious that there would be no photography that day, so Jackie and I caught up with the rest of the class and attended the day's lectures as scheduled.

We did complete our assignment as film stars the following day. It went very smoothly and quickly with no one talking to one another. Captain Penner told Slate Hardman he wouldn't let him produce the film versions of his books if Hardman were the last producer on earth.

"Not only that," Penner threatened as he dropped the Hardman crew at the airport, "I ought to tell the Air Force how you cheated them with this family you call a crew."

"Do that, you hack soldier, and I'll tell them you write pornies on the side."

"Just until my first novel clicks," Penner said with pride.

"Clicks?" Hardman belched. "You're a bum. A bum in blue."

"And you're a fat beard."

"Shut your mouth, Penner, or I'll . . ."

Clyde jumped between the men and put an end to the fight.

"Don't sweat it, Pop. If he makes trouble, we can always do FAA movies."

"That's right," his father agreed with a Stan Laurel nod to Penner. "And there's always the USIA after that."

On that note of optimism the Hardman family departed

116

for Milwaukee. They took with them the film to be edited into the finished nurse film, the 1600 feet of Ginger *au naturel,* and Captain Penner's seven works of leather-bound art which he forgot to retrieve.

Chapter 13

"Water . . . NOW—NOW—NOW"

The mayor's office estimated the demonstrators at three hundred. General Giddypate claimed there were five. By actual head count there were seventeen people:

Six college students
Five irate mothers
Four baby strollers
One real live baby
And the mayor with a scowl across his face.

They came on Saturday morning just as the full-scale base parade was about to begin. The student nurse group was lined up behind the new Air Force doctors who were going through their introduction to the military way. It was a brutally hot Texas morning, and everyone was grumbling and wiping their brows.

The band was tuned up to a degree and was about to strike the first note when the initial shout was heard from the direction of the gate. It drifted over the base and caused everyone to turn around, including General Giddypate and his associates on the reviewing stand.

"Water . . . NOW—NOW—NOW!" were the words from the gate.

General Giddypate dismissed the intrusion and signaled the band to begin. It followed his order with a loud beating of the bass drum and a staccato blare from the trumpets. The first unit marched off in step to the music. Then the next. And finally our group extended their left feet and fell into the parade's flow.

The chanting from the gate became louder as the parade progressed. It was obviously coming closer, and it wasn't long before the protesting group marched toward our parade. We began to panic as our little unit and the protesting unit began to converge. It became a question of who would relinquish and halt. We were approaching at right angles, Captain Alantean in charge of our group and Mayor Bilkhauser leading the demonstrators. It had come down to a matter of will between the two leaders. I shot a glance up at the reviewing stand and saw General Giddypate wince as Alantean and the mayor collided.

"Halt," she squawked as she fell to the ground on top of Mayor Bilkhauser.

"Stop," he ordered on the way down.

Both groups came to a standstill. We were eyeball to eyeball with the mothers and students. Between us lay Captain Alantean and Mayor Bilkhauser. The baby cried.

The students were a mean-looking lot. They had a lot of

hair and were pasty and thin. The mothers were plump and ruddy and wore too much lipstick. I noticed one student directly across from me had a whole row of oversized medals pinned on his silk T-shirt. They read: Berkeley, Columbia, Chicago Convention, New York Soupy Sales Rally, Selma, Calif.-Sexual Freedom League Rally, Calif.-Napalm Protest, and Up Yours Hoover March—NY. It was an impressive display of past campaigns. The other students, although not wearing medals of past glories, appeared to be as battle-hardened as the medal-bearing fellow.

One of the mothers, who was dressed in a blouse, slacks, and high heels and who wheeled an empty baby carriage, yelled at General Giddypate on the reviewing stand, "Pig! Water hog! Drought merchant!"

Giddypate disappeared behind two of his aides. He peeked around them and was subjected to another round of insults.

"Drown Giddypate!" a student and a mother screamed. "Dust up your nose, Giddypate!"

Mayor Bilkhauser had gotten up with the help of Captain Alantean and raised his hand to silence his demonstrators. The parade had come to a complete halt, and a stillness pervaded the dusty morning.

"General Giddypate," the mayor called out.

The general whispered something to his aide. The aide nodded agreement at what was said, climbed down off the stand and approached Mayor Bilkhauser. You could feel the tension build as all eyes focused on the mayor and the young officer-aide. The aide stopped a few feet in front of the mayor, and their eyes engaged in a mute battle of nerves and stamina. It was the aide who spoke first.

"General Rufus Giddypate asks what it is you want."

"I wish to speak with General Giddypate," the mayor responded in flat tones.

"Hmmmmm," the aide went. He did an about-face and returned to the general on the stand. They conferred. The aide returned.

"General Rufus Giddypate will see you in his office at the conclusion of the ceremonies."

"Nope. Right here. Right now."

"Hmmmmm," the aide went again. He went back to the reviewing stand and passed along the mayor's demands to the general. All eyes slowly turned to the stand in anticipation of what might develop. And then, his stomach securely sucked in and his hat planted a little more firmly on his head, General Rufus Giddypate slowly descended from the stand

and began walking toward Mayor Bilkhauser. We checked the mayor's face, and he seemed to look a little nervous, at least in comparison to his earlier steely posture and attitude. The general was halfway there when one of the airmen in the band, a drummer, began a slow roll on the snare. The band officer put a stop to that with one cold look.

General Giddypate reached Mayor Bilkhauser. They stared each other down for what seemed an eternity. The students tightened in readiness for battle. The mothers didn't seem to be sure what to do; they tightened their grips on the stroller handles. Captain Alantean hitched up her skirt in the Cagney manner. The only sound was Ginger: "Oh, my."

"Well?" General Giddypate said. Mayor Bilkhauser glanced around at the thousand or so airmen and officers. He looked at his students and mothers. His face twisted into a pained expression as he hunched his shoulders, managed a weak smile at the general, and said, "Come on, Rufus. Shut off the water, will ya?"

The general knew superiority was his. He smiled in triumph, cast a look of disgust at the students, and turned to face his troops.

"Resume the parade," he commanded in his finest voice.

The band played, we marched, and the students all yelled at once at Mayor Bilkhauser.

"Coward."

"Sellout."

"Up yours, Bilkhauser."

The baby cried and everyone went home.

Actually, the matter of the water scandal wasn't solved that easily. There was a Congressional probe the following November, according to a newspaper story we read. By then there was no drought. General Giddypate had been assigned to Washington as Commander of Domestic Community Affairs, and Mayor Bilkhauser was defeated in his bid for reelection by a young peace candidate. The new general at the base didn't like gardening, and the new mayor didn't like anything except girls. They've lived in peaceful coexistence ever since.

Chapter 14

"This Party Will Come to Order!"

Jackie was right. The days did become easier, the physical routine less strenuous, and we soon found ourselves within spitting distance of basic training's final few days. Naturally, this pleased us a great deal.

The classroom sessions proved themselves to be interesting and surprisingly stimulating. Slowly we became saturated with a sense of pride and mission; nursing in the military was played with big stakes, and dedication could carry you along in situations where more than simple nursing skill and physical stamina were needed.

The three weeks were capped by the "graduation" party held at the Officers' Club on the eve of our final day of training. The party was the source of much talk during the week leading up to it. These graduation parties had reputations of their own that carried over from class to class. It was acknowledged that they usually ended up in a rather impressive shambles despite the fact that each party was held only for the members of the graduating class. The party had been conceived as a quiet although happy dinner during which the girls would break bread, sip wine, and cement lasting friendships born but perhaps strained during the three weeks of close contact.

But we were told that at each party in the past things had gradually spread to include every officer who happened to be in the club that particular evening.

Either way—quiet dinner or swinging party—it was an event to be approached with joy and great expectations. Excitement ran high the week before the dinner, and by the time the great day rolled around, we were all like high school sophomores getting ready for the first prom. Well, all except Barbara Thompson, who was very disdainful of the whole affair.

"Just get me out of this place and back to civilization," she snorted when asked about the party. "I've never seen anything so cornball." We'd learned to tolerate Barbara's harshness and tough exterior. Scratch the veneer and you found even harsher stuff. It was easier to tolerate the surface material.

The hallway in the BOQ was truly a joyous sight the evening of the party. Everyone was milling around, going from room to room, looking for approval of the fit of the mess whites, hair styles, makeup.

"Big deal," Barbara said, never looking up from her magazine. "Who the hell are you all trying to impress? Each other?"

124

"Come on, Barbara," Jackie said. "There'll be a lot of people there. Besides, what's wrong with just wanting to look nice?"

"Nothing's wrong with it. It's just a waste of time unless you're trying to impress someone. I mean, if you're looking to get laid or something . . ."

"Oh, Barbara. You do have a one-track mind."

"You bet." She went back to concentrating on her reading. She'd already dressed and was just killing time.

By five-thirty we were all at the cocktail party and sipping our drinks. Captain Alantean was the sort of unofficial hostess for this phase of the evening's festivities and seemed to enjoy the chore. She was as gay as we'd ever seen her, especially when you consider her usual taciturn outlook on all things.

"Well, you certainly look pretty tonight, Ginger," she told our buxom classmate.

"Thank you, ma'am. I think it's very important for a nurse to look her best for her patients, don't y'all?"

"I think it probably helps, Ginger." They were joined by Captain Clarence Penner, information officer and novelist.

"Well, Captain Alantean, talking to our guinea pig here?" Penner smiled at Ginger.

She scowled back. "Now I don't think that's a very nice way to . . ."

"Just turning a phrase, Lieutenant Whip," Penner said. "I just got word that they've accepted my recommendation for you to be the nurse to attend a stewardess school. That's why I stopped in tonight."

Captain Alantean grunted and forced a smile. Ginger sort of fell apart, giggled, bit her lip, and finally whistled. "Me. You really mean li'l ol' me?"

"That's right, Ginger. It wasn't easy, but I can talk a pretty good argument. You'll be leaving for the stewardess school the day after tomorrow."

"I'm so excited, Captain Penner."

"Call me Clarence, Ginger. After all we've been through we can be friendlier than that."

"I certainly do agree. I just wish I could repay you in some meaningful way."

Penner grimaced. "Let's talk about that a little later, shall we, Ginger? Frankly, I do have something in mind." He left the private room, presumably to return to the bar.

"Ladies, let's adjourn now to the dining room." Captain Alantean made the announcement softly, but there was still a trace of the drill-field voice. We all proceeded to the next private room in which long tables had been set up in the classic horseshoe arrangement. We took seats at the place settings marked with our names. The head table filled up with the following lineup, from left to right: Harry, the partner, Abraham Lefkowitz, Captain Richard Monoman, Mayor Bilkhauser, (Empty Chair), Captain Alantean, Captain Ruttish.

"Good evening, girls," Alantean said after rising and tapping a water glass with her spoon. "And welcome to your graduation dinner. I'm very pleased to see you all here. I'd like to introduce the people at our head table before we begin with the fruit cup."

No one seemed to protest, so Alantean continued.

"This is a very special graduation dinner, girls. Never before have we been honored with the appearance of the mayor of this fair city, Mayor Monroe Bilkhauser." She looked down at him and beamed. He stood up halfway and gave a V-for-Victory sign and sat down again to thunderous applause.

"Unfortunately," Alantean continued, "General Giddypate is going to be detained. It's been his practice to attend every graduation dinner in the past. I assure you he'll be here for this one, too, although a little late." She again smiled at Mayor Bilkhauser. He avoided her look and kept his eyes on his fruit cup.

Alantean introduced Abraham Lefkowitz next. She billed him as a long-time friend of every nurse at the base. He stood up and launched into a speech which Alantean cut off quickly.

"We're going to eat first, Mr. Lefkowitz, and *then* have the speeches."

"Of course, of course." He sat down.

Alantean sighed and looked at Harry, who was looking at Ginger, who was looking at Captain Monoman, who was looking at Captain Ruttish.

"This is Harry. He works with Mr. Lefkowitz," Alantean continued.

"A partner," he said from his seat. He sounded grumpy. Alantean ignored him and went on to introducing Captain Monoman.

"Of course, each of you knows Captain Monoman. He's done his usual fine job as course supervisor for this class."

Monoman looked pained. Ginger threw a smile across the room, but Monoman successfully avoided it. It was an obvious attempt on Ginger's part and an obvious bit of avoidance by Monoman. Jackie and I looked at each other, and our thoughts went back to discussions we'd been having during the past two weeks. Those two weeks had seen Ginger dating Harry, the partner, almost exclusively. But she also had indulged in frequent daytime meetings with Captain Monoman.

While Ginger had cavorted with Harry, Ted Ruttish had made Marthas Trouble his personal habit. We could never figure this relationship; Ruttish and Ginger made a more sensible pairing of people. Many times, at the Officers' Club, open animosity would flare up between Ginger and Ruttish. They never really said anything, but their emotions were open, sparks and flames flashing back and forth. It was uncomfortable at times but interesting.

Captain Alantean got around to introducing Ted Ruttish. By that time we'd begun to realize that the choice of people at the head table was, at best, a strange one. What right did Ruttish have to be there? Or Lefkowitz and Harry? Alantean carried off the introductions, but she, too, seemed puzzled and a trifle upset at the assortment of partners seated at the head table.

"Well, introductions over with, we can eat our fruit." We applauded and picked the cherries off the top of our fruit cups.

"I just love cherries," Ruttish whispered to Alantean. He poked her in the ribs with his elbow and laughed dirty. She turned and gave him a look that would kill. He grunted and attacked the pears at the bottom.

The waiters came and took away the fruit cups. Barbara Thompson sat back in her chair, refolded her napkin and placed it on the table. Marthas, sitting next to her, shook her head and leaned over to her.

"You shouldn't have done that," she said.

"Done what?"

"Folded your napkin after you'd unfolded it."

"For Christ's sake, Marthas. Why not?"

"You'll never be invited back again by your hosts, Barbara."

Barbara roared. "Thank God," she said.

"You're very foolish," Marthas concluded.

The waiters served the pea soup. Only the people at the head table seemed to enjoy it. I looked around and noticed everyone had taken one or two spoonfuls and pushed the plate away.

"Isn't this grim?" Jackie whispered to me.

"Sure is. Like a wake."

It certainly was solemn. What had started as a gay cocktail party had quickly dissipated into a very formal and stiff dinner. The people at the head table spoke in hushed tones. Captain Monoman spoke to no one. Ruttish occasionally poked Alantean in the ribs, but she ignored him. The only interplay between the students and the head table came when Ginger asked Mayor Bilkhauser for his autograph.

"I bet someday when y'all in Congress or somethin', this autograph will be very valuable," she told him. He seemed genuinely pleased and wrote a very long note to Ginger on the back of the program. But despite the mayor's pleasure, Alantean didn't like what Ginger had done and made her feelings known with a hard stare.

By the time the Salisbury steak arrived, the atmosphere had become downright sullen. It was as though some little fairy had tiptoed into the room and sprinkled sleepy sand over each person present. Barbara Thompson let out a yawn that momentarily snapped everyone awake. But it lasted for only a few seconds.

We were almost finished with dessert—fruit salad over shortcake—when Captain Alantean stood up, plunked on the water glass with a gravy-stained fork, and said, "Attention, girls. It's time now for our honored speakers."

Alantean had spotted General Giddypate through the half-open door. He'd entered the club, stopped to chat with a few officers at the bar, and walked briskly into our room. We all stood immediately, but he smiled, motioned us to sit down, and slapped Mayor Bilkhauser on the back. It caught the mayor by surprise, and he spit out the last remaining piece of pear from dessert.

"I wish you wouldn't do that, Rufus," he muttered as he turned around and shook the general's hand.

"Good to have you here, Mr. Mayor," the general boomed. "Real honor for the girls."

Bilkhauser nodded.

It seemed that Captain Alantean was about to make some sort of introduction for General Giddypate. But he started right in on his talk. It was intended to be inspirational, and we suppose it was, to an extent. He began by citing various great thinkers of the past, linking each man's words to the challenge we would face as Air Force nurses. And as he spoke, it became obvious that, in his mind, the greatest challenge we would meet was that of a civilian population

128

not willing and able to understand the mission of the Armed Forces. As General Giddypate began making this point, Mayor Bilkhauser started to squirm in his seat. He ground his teeth and twitched a lot.

". . . the gravest danger we face today in this nation is a civilian population dedicated to the destruction of the military machine."

"That's not true!" Mayor Bilkhauser stood up and looked the general square in the eye. "There you go again, Rufus. Blaming us for everything. It just isn't fair."

General Giddypate shot an embarrassed look at us. We were wide-eyed—excitement at last!

"I don't think this is the place for such a . . ."

"Oh, shut up, Rufus. You'r nothing but a pompous windbag."

"Now w-a-i-t a m-i-n-u-t-e . . ."

The mayor was really turned on now. He looked at us, saw we were enraptured, and resumed his attack on General Giddypate.

"You hide behind that uniform and those stars. I wonder what these young people here would think if they weren't living under you as a . . . a . . . a dictator."

"Dismissed!" Alantean shouted to us. We didn't move.

"Furthermore," the mayor went on, "you won that argument about the water because you had all those men standing ready to kill."

The general shoved Mayor Bilkhauser in the chest.

"See?" the mayor yelled at us.

We dismissed, this time without even being told. We all headed for the bar, the sounds of loud arguing growing fainter in the background. A loud cheer rose from the bar.

"Hey, they sprung you," someone shouted. "Drinks for the nurses."

It was good to be free of the official dinner and its depressing atmosphere. Abraham Lefkowitz emerged from the private room, came directly to us, and muttered, "Some graduation. I had my speech all ready to be given and what happens? Two grown men act like kiddies. Aach! Never again will I accept an invitation." He waddled off, still mumbling under his breath.

"Poor old Lefkowitz," an officer commented. "He's invited to these dinners every time around, tries to give a speech, and Alantean shuts him off. I assume she did the same tonight."

"No," Jackie corrected him. "General Giddypate and Mayor Bilkhauser got in a fight."

"A real fight?"

"Yup. Pushing and all."

"Wow! That should raise some dust around here."

At that point General Giddypate stormed from the private dining room, nodded to greetings from officers at the bar, and left the club. He was followed shortly thereafter by Mayor Bilkhauser, who held his left eye and looked the other way as he passed the bar.

"Giddypate must have belted him," an officer commented.

"I hope so," a tough-looking colonel said. "These damn civilians meddle into military affairs and screw it all up."

No one seemed inclined to argue the point, so it died. We sipped our drinks. Ted Ruttish eventually came to the bar, followed by Harry, the partner, and Captain Monoman, in that order. Marthas immediately grabbed Ruttish by the arm and led him to a corner table. Ginger seemed perplexed. She didn't know whether to greet Harry or Monoman first. And Captain Penner was right there to make up her mind.

"Come on, Ginger," he said, "let's dance." She protested weakly, but he pulled her away from the bar and led her onto the dance floor. The combo had started their first tune of the evening, and soon the floor was filled.

"Well, what about it, Ginger?" Penner asked as they danced.

"What about what?" She was busy looking over his shoulder at Harry and Monoman at the bar.

"You and me, Ginger. We've experienced a great deal together. Now, through my work, you'll be leaving here soon for a new experience. But there's one experience we haven't shared yet, and we must share that one now. Tonight." His hand slowly massaged her buttocks, and she could feel him press closer to her.

"Now y'all just calm down, Captain Penner," Ginger cooed in his ear, still watching Harry and Monoman. "I certainly do like you, and you have been awful good to me. But I do have my reputation to think of. Now don't y'all go and forget that."

"I won't, I won't," he said in a husky, breathy voice. His mind went back to Ginger and Hardman's son at the motel. But he wouldn't bring that up. As far as Penner was concerned, Ginger was his for the night. Ever since he'd first laid eyes on her, he'd envisioned them in bed together. Lately, since the fifth book, he'd found himself having to stretch his

130

imagination in search of exotic and stimulating sex scenes. His wife was no help. But Ginger could lift him to great heights of personal and professional achievement. He was supremely confident of that.

"Let's go now, Ginger. I know just the motel."

Ginger noticed Harry growing increasingly impatient. Monoman, too, seemed anxious to leave. He kept glancing at his watch, and that was bad. Ginger had to speak to him right away.

"Clarence," she whispered in Penner's ear as the band went into another slow number, "I think I owe you a great deal. You go ahead to that spot y'all got picked out for us an' I'll join ya just as soon as I can. After all, it wouldn't look right for me to be flittin' off with ya so early in the evenin'."

"Yes, yes, discretion. I like that. You can count on it with me, too, Ginger."

Penner gave Ginger the name and address of the motel and set off in his car to make ready. In the meantime Ginger returned to the bar.

"Hi, Dick," Ginger greeted Monoman.

"Hello, Ginger," Harry answered.

"Oh, hello, Harry."

"I wanna talk to you."

"Not now, Harry. In a minute. Could I speak with *you*, Dick?" Ginger asked Monoman.

"W-w-w-well, I s-s-s-suppose so." Monoman looked around to see who was watching. His eyes met those of Marthas Trouble and Ted Ruttish. "C-c-c-couldn't we do it another time, Ginger?"

Ginger stamped her foot and pouted. "No. I wanna do it right now."

"Ginger . . ."

"Shut up, Harry."

Harry shut up. Ginger led Captain Monoman to a table in the far opposite corner from that occupied by Marthas and Ruttish.

"Do it now, Dick," she said to Monoman as soon as they sat down.

"I ch-ch-changed my m-m-mind, Ginger. I don't want to d-d-d-do it."

"You promised."

"I know, but I don't w-w-want to now."

Ginger pouted again. She looked across the room at Ted Ruttish. He was involved in a discussion with Marthas.

"Let's do it right now, Marthas baby."

131

"Don't call me baby. And I'll do it when I'm good and ready."

"Look, Marthas, tonight's the night. She leaves in a couple of days for that stewardess school. Now, Marthas. Please."

Marthas looked over at Ginger. Monoman looked over at Ted Ruttish.

"OK," Marthas told Ruttish with a sigh.

"All r-r-right," Monoman told Ginger.

While the ensuing agreements were reached at the Officers' Club, Captain Clarence Penner was busy setting up the motel room. He'd stopped and bought a bottle of Cutty Sark—the best Scotch, in his opinion. After checking in at the desk, he got ice from the machine, filled the pitcher with water, and found a station on the room radio playing soft music. Lights low, he carefully turned back the bedspread, stripped down to his pants, and took one last look in the mirror. With his stomach sucked in, he looked good in the dim light.

The sound of a car's wheels outside the motel sent him scurrying to the easy chair. He sat in it, crossed his legs, and waited for the knock on the door. But all he heard was giggling as a young man and girl entered the room next to his. Penner got up and went to the wall. He pressed his ear to it and heard the young man say, "I never did this before, Jane."

"Silly. Me neither. But we're gonna love it."

Penner broke out in a cold sweat. He ran back to the desk and grabbed a pencil and paper. Then he went back to the wall and listened as the young couple proceeded to make use of the motel room.

Meanwhile, back at the club, Marthas Trouble secretly reached into the handbag on her lap and fondled something inside. Ruttish tried to see what she had, but his vision was blocked by the table's edge.

"What are you doing?" he asked.

"Sh! Don't interrupt."

"OK. OK."

Around them, the party was beginning to roll; the room had jammed up and people were everywhere. But Marthas seemed to have lifted herself into her own world of quiet seclusion. Her eyes took on a glaze, and her head moved in small, almost indiscernible circles.

"Ommmmmm . . . ommmmmm," she chanted in the lowest of tones.

132

Ted Ruttish started to panic. He looked around and was relieved to see that no one was paying any particular attention to Marthas and her ritual.

"Hurry up, will you?" he said.

"Ommmmmmm."

"Jeez."

Across the room, Captain Richard Monoman had fallen into his own trance. He licked his lips and allowed his eyes to float to the top of their sockets.

"Are y'all all right?" Ginger whispered.

"O-o-o-ommmmmmmm," he answered.

"Oh, my."

Ginger looked over at Ted Ruttish.

"He still looks the same," she said to Monoman. "Faster."

"I'm t-t-trying, Ginger," he replied. "O-o-o-ommmmm," he went again.

Ted Ruttish looked across the room at Ginger.

"She doesn't look any different to me," he said to Marthas in a surly voice. She hissed at him and brought her hand up from beneath the table. Ruttish looked down at a tiny doll. It possessed a huge bosom, had blond hair, and looked very much like Ginger Whip.

"Come on, baby," he pleaded with Marthas.

No one else in the room was aware that these two mystics were filling the air with mysterious static, forbidden curses, and powerful potions of mental strength. Monoman leaned toward Ruttish as if to shorten the distance between their respective brains. Marthas kneaded and caressed the Ginger-doll.

"Make her want me, baby," Ruttish moaned to Marthas. "Make her beg for it."

The witchcraft at the base had not affected Clarence Penner at the Bubbling Creek Motel. He scribbled faster and faster as the action in the next room became more intense.

"It's just like in *The Valley of the Dolls*," the girl could be heard to say.

"I didn't read that," the boy said with heavy breathing.

"I'll show you, Howard."

Penner wiped the sweat from his brow and went on to the next sheet of paper.

The tension between Marthas Trouble and Richard Monoman was reaching its peak. Ruttish was mad and Ginger was scared. Ruttish was annoyed at how long it was taking. After all, he just wanted Marthas to cast a spell on

133

Ginger so she'd get rid of Harry, the partner, and be totally receptive to any advances Ruttish might make. He had no way of knowing that Ginger had the same thing in mind when she went to Richard Monoman. She asked him to cast a spell on Ruttish to cause him to fall in love with her. She'd never met a more handsome and exciting man in her life. Her public attachment to Harry, the partner, was a tactic calculated to fan the fires of jealousy in Ted Ruttish. But time was short. If she was to have Ted Ruttish, she'd have to have him now, especially since he had a wife and five children who would have to be dealt with.

Ruttish winced as his bad ankle twinged with pain. He'd challenged Marthas Trouble that night. He'd called her a fraud. And she'd done two things that surprised him. She went to bed with him in her BOQ room. And she accepted his challenge.

"I suppose it's time to prove my powers to a nonbeliever," she'd said as he dressed.

"You proved one power to me, Marthas baby," he told her. "You're one hell of a piece."

"Don't be crude. I detest crudity. It was simply necessary for me to come as close as possible to you before undertaking this challenge. Frankly, I prefer a more gentle man."

That's when Ruttish went out the window, fell, and hurt his ankle.

Ginger's approach to Captain Monoman was different. In effect, she'd blackmailed the poor, stuttering man who fell completely apart when confronted by Marthas. Ginger had told him she knew all about his hang-up (she didn't really, but pleaded a good case), and promised to keep Marthas out of his hair if he'd cooperate with her on this one request. To Ginger's thinking, she couldn't miss, not with a mystic applying cosmic power and Harry supplying basic human powers of jealousy.

"Ommmmmmmmm," went Marthas.

"O-o-o-o-ommmmmm," went Monoman.

And Harry fell off the bar stool. He hit with a loud THUD, and a few people screamed and yelled.

"He's dead," someone said.

"He's drunk," another answered.

It made little difference at the moment why Harry fell on the floor. The result was a complete breaking of the spell. Ruttish and Ginger jumped up from their respective tables and joined the crowd gathered around Harry. He lay there in a fetal position, a silly grin affixed to his face. He wasn't dead. Drunk was the correct diagnosis.

Marthas Trouble got up from the table and walked over to Monoman. "Casting a spell, Captain?" she asked.

"Y-y-y-yes."

"Me, too. Shall we dance?"

The band started playing again to return the crowd to some order. Marthas led Monoman to the empty dance floor, put his arm around her, and they shuffled off together.

Ruttish gave Ginger's arm a pinch as they watched two TDY officers drag Harry off to the manager's office.

"What'd I tell you, Ginger, sweetie?" he said with a smug smile. "I told you to stay away from these drunken woman-chasers. Look at him. Disgraceful."

Ginger looked up into Ruttish's bloodshot eyes. "I guess you were right, Ted. I certainly should have listened to you. Oh, my, yes."

"Well, let's forget about it, doll. Dance?"

"I'd love to."

Ginger and Ruttish joined Marthas and Monoman on the dance floor.

"Look at that," Ruttish whispered to Ginger. "I really can't understand that Trouble broad. Everybody on the base knows Monoman is a nut."

"All I've got to say after livin' with that girl for three weeks is that she certainly is a strange and unusual person. That's really Marthas' trouble. She's just so different."

"Yeah."

Tango.

Meanwhile, back at the Bubbling Brook Motel, Captain Penner had consumed half of the Cutty Sark and filled up four pages of notes. The couple, Jane and Howard, had departed, with Jane saying, "Gee, that's sure better than necking in the car." Howard agreed. Their place had been taken by another couple who were older and more experienced.

"I'm gonna read the *Kama Sutra* to ya while we do it," the man told the woman.

"Read one of mine," Penner murmured in a drunken slur.

Penner went to bed after the third couple had successfully used the room. He'd forgotten all about Ginger. His only thought as sleep came was the title he'd use on his next book.

"Motel Masochist, Motel Masochist," he said over and over. "Not bad, not bad."

All in all, the party turned out to be a huge success. Once the spells were broken and Harry was securely asleep on the couch, everyone launched into a concerted effort to have the maximum fun in the minimum time. After many drinks, much dancing, and a rousing round of community singing, we headed for a colonel's home in town for beer and pizza. We all got to bed at six the following morning and slept until two that afternoon. At three we had a meeting with Captain Alantean, who announced our assignments. Jackie and I had requested and been given assignments to Flight Nursing School. We'd have a week's leave before reporting.

Alantean also announced that Ginger was going to stewardess school, which brought lots of laughs to the group. Marthas was assigned to Washington, D.C., where she could practice her strange rituals on our Congress and her patients. Ginger would join us at Flight Nursing School after her stint at stewardess school.

"We'll see you at flight school," we said to Ginger after the meeting had broken up.

"Oh, my, yes. I'm just so thrilled and all."

"Now don't go losing your head and join the airline."

"Oh, my, no, ma'am."

We'd started to walk away when Ginger stopped us with, "I just can't contain myself any longer. I've just got to tell y'all the other good news."

"What's that, Ginger?"

"Captain Ruttish asked me to marry him."

Our stunned expressions were legitimate. We were stunned.

"But he's married, Ginger. At least that's what we've heard. Five kids, too."

"I know that, and I feel just downright awful about it. I mean for his wife and all. But she certainly hasn't been a very good wife to him, poor dear. She doesn't understand him at all. Not a bit."

We smiled, offered best wishes, and went back to our rooms.

"Do you know what, Joni?" Jackie said as she undressed and was stepping into the shower.

"What?"

"I'm really happy that I've gotten to meet Ginger Whip. Really happy. I'd always heard about girls like that but just never believed they existed."

"Oh, they exist, all right. In the flesh."

136

"That's not funny," Jackie said and turned on the water.

"You're right. It isn't funny," I yelled over the sound of the spray. "But it is a lot of laughs."

I started packing.

Chapter 15

"My Report"

Ginger went to stewardess school for one week, as promised by Captain Penner. She has taken her place in history as the first woman from the United States Air Force to do so, and is thus assured lasting remembrance by her peers and those to follow. At least that's the way Captain Penner put it to her just before she left.

"Come, Ginger, and let us crown this glorious moment by giving to each other our deepest and most precious gifts . . . our bodies and vital passionate forces."

"Why, that's just beautiful," she responded. "Just like outa some book a poetry or even a movie. Bless you, and say a little prayer for li'l ol' me." She kissed him on the cheek and ran to the airplane that would take her to an unnamed stewardess school somewhere deep in the American heartland.

Of course, there's no need to feel bad about Captain Penner. It wasn't over yet. The catch to Ginger's trip was that she would have to write a full report when she returned, detailing her experiences at stewardess school and evaluating the worth of the experiment.

"We'll create it together, Ginger," Penner told her. "Together we might even come up with the beginnings of the Great American Novel."

"Oh, my."

Ginger returned from her week at stewardess school and sat down with Penner to write her report. They had only one day in which to complete the work.

"Ginger, we have so much to do in one day," Penner whispered in her ear at the motel. He'd taken the room to ensure quiet while they created. "But I'm so keyed up. Let me take you, love you, enter your innermost privacy and start the creative juices flowing."

Ginger coughed in his face. She'd caught a cold during her week, and she was coughing and sneezing a great deal.

"Cover your mouth when you cough, Ginger." Penner popped two aspirin in his mouth. "And wipe your nose. It's running."

"Oh, my. They'd never approve a that at stewardess school."

The two of them went to work on the report. Ginger suggested an opening for it.

"I thought I'd begin the report by sayin' my name and tellin' what happened on my first day."

Penner said that would be nice but suggested he write the opening because the first paragraph would be the most im-

140

portant and set the scene for the rest of the report. Ginger agreed with this and told him of events on that first day.

"I got on the airplane and we had the nicest trip with alcoholic beverages and good food and such a pretty sight from way up there. They picked me up in a big black car when we landed and took me right away to that school. It was big and had a fence all the way around it and looked just like one a those mansions in the movies."

Penner went to work. He'd gotten the first sentence written when Ginger interrupted him.

"What's that book y'all keep lookin' at?"

"It's called *Roget's Thesaurus*. It has words in it."

"Just like a dictionary."

Penner nodded and continued with his writing.

At the end of the day the report was completed. Captain Penner had written the first few pages, tired of it, and had gone to work on his latest book while Ginger completed the report. The finished work was printed and distributed throughout the service, not officially but by an airman in the office for whom the report was intended. He did a fast mimeo job, and it has since become a priceless item in the files of many Air Force people looking for enjoyable bits of memorabilia from their military days. We present the report now in its entirety, including both Captain Penner's beginning and Ginger's subsequent completion of the work:

MY REPORT
By Lieutenant Ginger Whip
SUBJECT: Special TDY to Stewardess School
PURPOSE: Grooming and poise training
APPROVAL: Experimental
CLASSIFICATION: Secret [it has since been declassified]

I approached my role in this *ballon d'essai* with a substantial although controllable consternation, born of my intrinsic sensibilities and experiences but not limited to those undissimulating and refractory portions of my life, although it should be admitted that I have always been considered an excrutiatingly sensorial homo sapiens and thus it is potentially credible that more than the average aggregate of self-inflicted and self-perpetuated putations have played a superior farceur in this exciting, vital, challenging, forward-looking, crucial, and paramount experiment.

NOTE: (Speculation is that Ginger complimented Penner at

this point for truly capturing what she was thinking and feeling. He accepted her thanks graciously, tried to cop a feel and was rebuffed.

REPORT CONTINUES:

My initial cerebrations upon viewing the elephantine silver bird with long, sleek body and overpowering span of razor-tipped, clean patagiums was one of profound and moving reverence: to fly, perchance to soar to God's playground among angelic cherubs floating through the infinite grace of the azure hyaline, free as a warbler and my most divine spirit.

NOTE: ("I could cry," was probably Ginger's reaction upon reading the second paragraph.)
NOTE NUMBER TWO: (It becomes evident now that Captain Penner tired of thumbing through the thesaurus and turned to his own, more familiar work, leaving Ginger to complete the report. Perhaps he told her he had effectively set the scene for her and suggested they "lay down together to maintain the poetic mood." Ginger might have answered that "to lay down would break the poetic mood. Later, honey, later.")

REPORT CONTINUES:

We landed at the airport near the school, and a big black car picked me up. The driver was very nice. He looked like my father. He took me to the school. It was very pretty and had lots of trees and lots of flowers and a big fence all around the school and the trees and the pretty flowers. They told me not to touch the fence because it was electric and would kill me. I didn't touch the fence. I think we should have electric fences around the Air Force bases so spies cannot come in and steal the important secrets. I hope you accept my suggestion. It would be a good idea.

I lived in a room with three other girls. They were very nice and wanted to be airline stewardesses. I didn't like one to much, although, because she thought she was hot stuff and sexy and always walked around with her clothes off showing off. So what? I didn't even look except the first time. I don't think this is very nice. I am glad the girls in the Air Force don't act that way.

They make the girls at stewardess school work very hard. But they do not work as hard as we work in the Air Force. They do not do exercises to build strong bodies. They do not march around and count out loud to become good buddies. They smoke a lot and always talk about boys and all the men they will meet when they fly on the airplanes. I did not even listen since I was so busy studying and doing good in my classes except for the first time they talked this way and I said SO WHAT.

Everybody liked me and my uniform. They said it looked sharp. I said I liked there uniforms likewise and even since I really did not like there uniforms I wanted to be kind and make a good impression for the Air Force. I did make a good impression for the United States Air Force and for my nursing profession. You could be proud of me. I was kind and smiled a lot. They like that because all stewardesses smile a lot even when they are mad and grumpy due to female disorders and being tired.

I was lucky to go to the stewardess school. I went to classes about how to look pretty and the teacher said I all ready did look pretty. I made a good impression for the United States Air Force and for my nursing profession.

I would like to make a suggestion and it is not to make the nurses who follow after me to stewardess school go to some of the classes about good poise. They made me walk with a heavy book on my head and it hurt a lot and when it fell off my head they would get mad. But they smiled when they were mad so I guess it is not so bad as I thought it was bad.

Nurses in the United States Air Force are much more healthy than the girls who want to be stewardesses. They are skinny and the teachers make them get skinnier and skinnier. They said I wasn't skinny enough and that my hips were to wide but I explained we eat a lot in the United States Air Force and are healthy to take care of wounded United States Air Force men in the war and they never said I was too fat again. I made a good impression for the United States Air Force and my nursing profession.

The girls who want to be stewardesses do not follow orders as good as we follow orders in the United States Air Force. They are not allowed to read a book about them. It is called *Coffee Tea or Me?* and is supposed to be very dirty and not true. But some of the girls have that book under there pillows and read it at night and giggle a lot. I did not read it since I was there and should follow orders, even since I am a United States Air Force Nurse and not a United States Airline Stewardess. You can be proud of me.

I learned a lot. The commanding teacher said I was the

143

most unusual and mercurial AND THAT IS EXACTLY
WHAT SHE SAID girl she ever had at the school.

I believe it is a good idea to send the nurses to stewardess
school since this is a good chance to tell other people about
the United States Air Force and my fellow nurses. I did tell
everybody and they listened to me.

Thank you for sending me.

Officially:
Ginger Whip
Lieutenant
United States Air Force Nurse

Chapter 16

"This Is a Fine Time to Tell Us You Get Airsick"

Jackie and I proudly set off for our six-week training course in Aeromedical Evacuation at Brooks Air Force Base, Texas. We each went home during the one-week leave period prior to reporting and saw our friends, slept late, chatted with family about our new experiences, and showed off our uniforms a great deal. Jackie said she had the most marvelous time strutting around her home town in uniform. She passed right by Willard, and he wouldn't even look at her. He just pretended he was looking at the bras in the store window.

We were both looking forward to the leave, but although it was enjoyable for both of us, there was a deep yearning to get on with the next phase of our training and Air Force career. We were hooked. We liked being officers in the Air Force, and that's all there was to it.

Reporting to Brooks AFB was a lot easier than reporting for basic training—at least for me. Everything moved with crisp military precision, and we immediately felt at home and a part of the class. We also knew within the first few hours that this would not be an easy six weeks. The books and reference materials handed us as we processed in were enough to frighten off even a veteran scholar. Massive loose-leaf notebooks, training manuals, check-out lists and forms, textbooks, and ready-reference pamphlets weighed us down as we carried them back to our BOQ.

Naturally, classroom learning was to make up the bulk of the six weeks. But there were two areas of active participation and training that loomed as both challenging and frightening. One was the actual air evacuation flights to be made in real airplanes. The other was the three-day field exercise during which we would take to the fields of Texas, tents and all, and live the hard life of downed medical evacuation units. And it was a co-ed exercise, no less.

"Maybe I'll find my dream man," Jackie quipped the first evening over a drink in the Officers' Club (we found the club immediately after finding our rooms and latrines). "After all, if you can live for three days in a tent with a man, you can live with him forever . . . I think."

I told Jackie I was sure we wouldn't actually be living and sleeping in the same tent with the men. But then I wasn't sure. Maybe we would. That could be fun. Naughty. Verrrry interesting.

They didn't waste any time getting us ready for our first aeromedical evacuation flight. Classroom schedules were tight and demanding. Classroom emphasis was split between the procedures for working air evac, and basic although

146

complex medical procedures we might be called upon to perform at any time. At least we had to recognize symptoms and know how to deal with them.

We learned all about the physics of the atmosphere, which is vital when you're performing medical procedures at altitude in an aircraft. The effects of atmosphere can be devastating on certain types of patients. We learned how to spot kidney failure, heart failure, eye failure, lung failure, loss of consciousness, loss of reason, and even loss of good manners, which could indicate a mental problem of sorts.

There was so much to know, and even though we'd learned a great deal of the medical material while training in civilian life, it seemed now as if we knew nothing. The instructors pushed ahead at a fantastic rate with little time for repeating anything. We can recall only one exception—an assistant instructor in Cranial-Cerebral Injuries II, who devoted himself to the role of tutor for Ginger Whip, again our classmate and companion.

"Oh, my, I just don't understand what to do when a poor boy with pressure on the brain is in the airplane and we have to take off in a great big hurry. Now what is it again? I just never can rememba if his head goes to the front of the plane or to the rear of the plane. Silly ol' dumb me."

And the instructor would hover over Ginger at her desk and say things slowly and pat her shoulder to give her more confidence.

"I went steady once with somebody who had pressure on the brain," she told the instructor. "Poor dear boy."

Ginger and the tutor started dating and became a regular duo at the club in the evenings. We assume she did get it straight eventually about which way a pressure-on-the-brain patient was supposed to be placed on an aircraft in the event of short or accelerated takeoff. We hope she got it straight, for the patient's sake. Put him the wrong way and he's in for trouble under those circumstances.

We worked hard in class, knowing everything we learned would be put to use on that monumental day when we'd board the C-54 and actually take part in an Air Evac Training Mission. The tension was almost as crushing as preparing for the graduation party at Basic Training.

Finally the big day arrived. It was a clear morning as we reported to operations for the flight. It was scheduled to take us from nearby Kelly Air Force Base to Lowrey Air Force Base, and back again. Three of us were assigned to work the flight to Lowery and three to work it back home. The

147

remaining students would be patients, each with an assigned name, rank, and injury or disease. These student-patients would actually be placed on litters on the aircraft and, after we were airborne, present symptoms to the working nurses to see if they had learned their lessons. It was like beginning one big game of cops and robbers, and a strong competitive spirit prevailed by the time we boarded the plane.

I was to be a working nurse on the outbound leg to Lowrey. Jackie was to work the trip back. Ginger Whip was to play patient on both legs; she seemed pleased with the thought of lying down all the way.

Another student who would act as a patient was a friend of Ginger. Her name was Carla Schwartz, a big buxom girl with long black hair and a very wide fanny that moved considerably, never inhibited by any restraining undergarment of any kind. Ginger and Carla presented a formidable sight when walking together, no matter from what direction they were viewed. Carla, unlike Ginger, was a hypochondriac of the highest order. She constantly complained of aches and pains, spasms, tingles, strains, and a variety of other unreal symptoms. Carla's difficulties became a joke, and no one ever dared ask how she was.

Everything about the Air Evac Training Mission was very secret. The nurses didn't know what ills the student patients would come up with, and although those of us assigned to work the flight tried to coax some hints from the others, our pleas fell on deaf ears. They weren't saying.

"Lots of luck," was the way they summed up their feelings after we'd ask for a hint.

"Just don't forget," we'd answer, "your turn is coming." There were to be four training flights during the six weeks, and each of us would be playing both roles.

We all piled on board the C-54, the patients taking their places in their assigned litters and those of us playing nurse strapping ourselves in the seats placed on board for medical personnel.

The pilot, a lieutenant, taxied away from the parking apron, swung out onto the active runway, and soon had us airborne and heading for Lowrey Air Force Base. We reached cruise altitude of nine thousand feet and leveled off. And that was the signal for the exercise to begin.

The instructor on the flight handed us a clipboard with a list of students' names and the ills assigned each of them. Our first job was to decide where to place each patient in the aircraft. Those with suspected spinal and head injuries were

148

to be placed in the most stable parts of the plane, over the wings if possible. Mental patients were to be placed in the far aft section where they would be isolated from the others. Those with the most serious injuries and illnesses were to be in lower litter positions for easy access.

It took us much too long to decide where to place people. Our instructor kept looking at his watch and scowling—a sure sign we were fouling things up.

Ginger was causing us the most trouble. Appropriately, she'd been assigned acute kidney failure as her illness. But they also noted she might be slightly schizophrenic.

Carla Schwartz's stated malady was yellow jaundice. There was also a fractured skull, a broken leg, a shrapnel wound case, two shock patients, a manic depressive, a heart failure, and even one venereal disease played by Matilda Chaste, the class defender of pure personal living. Quite understandably, she was distressed to be chosen to play a venereal disease victim.

"I think it was a deliberate trick, and I don't think it's a bit funny," she told the instructor.

"Well, that'll teach you, Matilda," Jackie said.

"Teach me what?"

"Not to fool around."

Matilda was tight-lipped from that moment forward and was even surly when we'd ask her if she had any discomfort, where it was, and how she'd received her wound.

We eventually placed the patients in what we felt were the proper spots of the aircraft. And then the real trouble started.

One of the girls playing a patient, a bright and vivacious redhead named Jane, called me over to her litter. She'd been assigned shrapnel wounds in the head and shoulder.

"Nurse," she said, "I'm having trouble. My pulse rate is increasing and irregular, my breathing is irregular, and I seem to be lapsing into states of unconsciousness."

A challenge. She was giving me the "Triad of Trouble" we'd gone over in class. I couldn't think. I didn't want to think because there was so much to consider and remember, so many things to do and not to do.

But then I experienced a strange reaction. Suddenly Veronica Lake's face flashed before me. I saw the anguished faces of every actor killed and wounded in old movies. And then, to my surprise, the student before me was no longer a student. She was Kirk Douglas, and we were escaping the Japanese on Bataan.

"Oxygen," I ordered another nurse. While the other nurse

applied the oxygen mask to Jane, I got on the intercom and told the pilot we had a possible severe head injury in the back.

"Maintain altitude, sir," I barked, "and avoid turbulence if possible."

I took him by surprise.

"Roger," he replied.

"Over and out!"

Jane ripped the mask from her face.

"I'm in pain. I'm in a lot of pain."

"Morphine?" one of the other nurses suggested.

"Negative," I answered. I was right. We were taught never to give narcotics of any kind to a suspected head wound patient.

"Keep the oxygen going and check her every ten minutes," I ordered. Surprisingly enough, she did what I told her to do. I felt a little embarrassed giving orders like that, but it all seemed so natural. Of course, I'd find out when we landed whether or not I'd done the right thing. The instructor would see to that.

Jane was only the first student-patient to present a problem. Soon, on cue, everyone was coming up with new symptoms. It became a frantic and chaotic scene aboard the aircraft. The three of us were running everywhere, trying to diagnose, trying to make the right decisions, and trying to keep up with things in general. We were doing all right, too, until one of us three working nurses, a frail little gal, suddenly left a litter patient and raced for a barf bag. She must have vomited for at least ten minutes, and finally she pulled her head out of the bag and started crying.

"Hey, honey," I said, "what are you crying for? There's nothing wrong with getting sick."

"Yes, there is," she sobbed. "I always get sick, especially in airplanes. I just knew I'd get sick today, and they'll probably wash me out. Oops, excuse me." She headed for another barf bag and went at it again.

The two of us still on our feet and functioning worked that much harder to keep up with the myriad patient problems on the plane. We did pretty well, too, considering the number of symptoms that popped up. We were sure of one thing—a real air evac flight with real casualties would never be as rough as this training flight.

Matilda developed what we were sure was internal bleeding on top of her VD.

"What kind of a pig did you end up with, Matilda?" we asked her.

"Oh, shut up."

"Didn't you ever watch those movies, soldier?"

"I said shut up."

"You just can't fool around with the natives, Matilda."

Matilda, such as she was, called the instructor over and asked her to put a stop to our ridiculing her. The instructor made a show of compliance but winked at us when we walked away.

Then Carla started in.

"Ooooooh," she moaned.

"What's the matter with you?" I asked.

"My stomach," she said. "It hurts so."

"No kidding? Any other symptoms?"

"I feel . . . I feel . . . I feel nauseous."

I racked my brain for possible problems that would be indicated by Carla's symptoms. They could indicate many things.

"Well, you just relax, soldier," I comforted her, "and we'll be at the base soon." I made a mental note not to allow Carla to take anything by mouth, and to have a barf bag close by. I passed the word along, noted my thoughts on a chart, and put the barf bag next to Carla.

Confident that I'd done all that could or should be done, I went on to the next patient. But I turned back to Carla when I heard her making vomiting noises. She had her head over the bag and was going through all the motions and sound effects of someone actually throwing up. I shook my head.

"Boy, that Carla really plays the role all the way, doesn't she?" I muttered to the other working nurse.

She laughed. "I always knew she was a phony through and through."

I glanced back at Carla; she was lying down on the litter again. I went over and took the barf bag away. To my surprise, it was full.

"Ooooooooh," Carla moaned.

I went back to her.

"Come on, Carla, get off it, will you?" I whispered.

"Ooooooooh. My stomach."

I looked around to make sure the instructor wasn't within listening distance.

"Hey, Carla, do me a favor, will you? I'll do the same for you when you're working one of these training flights. Shut up! OK? Just shut up. You're a great actress and all that, but enough is enough."

"'But I'm sick. I really did throw up, didn't I?"

"Sure. And I think it's damn nasty of you to go so far as to stick your finger down your own throat."

"I didn't. I didn't stick my finger down my throat. Honest."

"Yes, you did, damn it. Or you just got airsick. Now shut up so I can do what I'm supposed to do."

Carla just moaned again, doubled up on the litter, and held her stomach. She moaned all the way down through the approach, all during landing and roll-out, and continued even after the doors had been opened and people started filing out of the aircraft.

"Oh, my," Ginger said as she cast one last, lingering look back at Carla. "I wonder if she's gone and taken all this so seriously that she's become de . . . de . . ."

"Demented?" Jackie offered.

"Yes. That's exactly it. Demented."

It turned out not to be true. Carla *did* have an attack of appendicitis. They operated on her at Lowrey and she rejoined us three weeks later. The lack of belief in Carla's moans and groans is funny to us in retrospect. But it wasn't to Carla. She refused to speak to me from that moment forward. I suppose she was especially annoyed that I received a commendation from the instructor for my performance on the training flight. After all, I did correctly diagnose Carla as having appendicitis.

On the three subsequent flights, I played the roles of a leg fracture, an eye injury, and a VD case. Matilda took great delight in kidding me about the reversal in roles. At least she tried.

"VD, huh? (Ho-ho-ho) Guess you've been fooling around."

"Yes, I have. Better not touch me. It's highly contagious."

We continued with our classroom training as well as the training flights. We covered so many subjects in those six weeks: burns, infection, new automation techniques, search and rescue, psychiatric care, resuscitation techniques, ionizing radiation, communicable diseases, drugs, ulcer care, surgical procedure, battlefield surgical procedure, transfusion under battle, cardiac care, amputation techniques, and even the legal aspects of military nursing, including the hows and whys of malpractice insurance.

"We'd never be sued, would we?" Ginger asked during the latter class.

"You never know," was the answer. We dismissed it as

nonsense. Besides, we were about to engage in the three-day field exercise, the one in a real field. The anticipation of that filled our heads and left little room for worrying about a wounded GI suing us for malpractice.

Basically, the field exercise is designed to simulate a wartime condition. It isn't inconceivable that we would end up in the field someday, perhaps Vietnam, or perhaps another trouble spot where people shoot at each other and casualties result. Of course, they couldn't teach us how to avoid a bullet. But the three days in some Texas fields would give us a taste of roughing it, a taste that might come in handy if the real thing ever came along.

Naturally, the main topic of conversation was the male personnel who would accompany us. These were med-techs, medical technicians who are the proverbial right hand to all military nurses. In some ways these male med-techs are roughly equivalent to hospital orderlies in civilian life. But in reality they are called upon to do much, much more than an orderly. Besides doing all the hard, heavy slop work, they also perform many medical procedures, much to the chagrin of some patients who've fallen victim to the few incompetent med-techs.

But by and large, these men and boys do a hell of a job, and more than one wounded GI in battle can chalk up his life to a courageous and proficient med-tech.

The med-techs were going through various courses at Brooks. Many were also involved in air evac training. Just about every flight we worked on had some med-techs on board to help care for the patients.

Other med-techs were going through courses in other fields of military medicine. Med-techs work in base hospitals and in front-line medical units and in just about any other area of medicine you'll find in the Armed Forces.

Some of our classes were co-ed, and as we began earnest preparation for the three-day field exercise, we saw more and more of the men.

"Aren't they just yummy?" Ginger said.

"They look like uncouth animals to me," was Matilda's response.

Despite our prejudgments, the men of the unit came with us on the field trial. We gathered at 0400 (that's 4 A.M.) and piled into trucks. There were more than a hundred of us, mostly male, and Ginger was in rare form despite the early hour and the chill that hung close to the ground and made us shiver.

"My goodness, I've never been so cold in all my natural life," she said to a handsome young med-tech. He smiled and put his arm around Ginger as they sat in the rear of the truck.

"Don't you worry 'bout a thing," the med-tech told her. "I'll keep you as warm as toast."

"Oh, my, what a gentleman. And so clever. As warm as toast. I've never heard anything so clever."

The med-tech adopted a shy pose and said, "I'm a writer. That's what I'll go back to when I'm finished with my military service."

"Now isn't that just the most amazin' thing I ever heard? Why, I was goin' steady once with a writer. An Air Force man, too. He wrote novels, and I'm gonna be the heroine in the next one he writes."

The airman looked at Ginger and smiled a knowing smile. "I'm working on a novel, too. There might be a place for you in my novel."

"Oh, my, two novels. I'm afraid it'll just all go to my head, and then what?"

He gave her a squeeze as the truck jerked to a start. It was obvious Ginger was off on another romp.

The cold morning air really penetrated our fatigue jackets, and we all sat shivering as the trucks rolled on to our destination. Everyone sat quietly and allowed their teeth to chatter and their knees to knock until a lonely-looking med-tech at the front of the truck reached into his duffel bag and brought out a guitar.

"Yeah! Music!" we shouted. It seemed to frighten the airman, because he quickly put the guitar back in the bag.

"Come on, play for us," we urged.

He looked so shy and afraid. But after looking around for any sign of displeasure, he reached back into the bag and again took out the guitar. He tuned it, blew on his hands, cleared his throat, and launched into his first number of the morning. It was a slow, plaintive melody, the guitar played with a grating twang, and his voice was a nasal whine riding over the truck's steady drone.

"Mah pappy grows the turnips and mah mammy washes clothes ... Mah doggy chases rabbits and mah sister likes ta sew ... Mah uncle is a drunkard and mah friend steals all mah gold ... Ah'm just a poor ol' sonabitch ..."

Everyone was prepared to scream in delight and encourage

154

the airman to go on. But his last line and the song's message were somehow at odds with mustering that kind of enthusiasm. No one said a word. The guitar player looked around the truck and inhaled noisily. We all sort of grinned at him, which, evidently, was enough to send him into a second chorus, this one with a rousing, foot-stomping rhythm:

"Mah teacher calls me stupid and mah girl friend says Ah smell ... The sheriff says Ah'm crooked and mah brother gives me hell ... The Army says Ah'm one-A and the doc says soon Ah'll die ... Ah'm just a poor ol' sonabitch."

Second chorus completed, the singing med-tech looked at us with a shy grin. We applauded. We had to.

"Say, that's right nice a you folks," he drawled. "Right nice."

"I never heard that song before," Jackie said.

"Shucks, Ah reckon you didn't, ma'am. Ah wrote it. Wrote some others, too."

There was nothing to do but ask to hear them. There was a tune about H-Bombs contaminating cow's milk. One dwelled on whether God liked snakes better'n humans. There was a snappy riff about a boy and girl whose love was thwarted by the homosexual god of the forest. And as a sort of grand finale the singing airman swung into a rousing chorus of the following, sung roughly to the tune of *The Battle Hymn of the Republic*:

"Ah went in to the city packin' virtue on mah back,
Ah went in to the city packin' virtue on mah back,
Ah went in to the city packin' virtue on mah back,
But some dirty pros-ti-tute relieved mah load!

"All mah morals are behind me, All mah morals are behind me ..."

And so on.

Someone asked the airman if he knew songs like *Down by the Old Mill Stream, For He's a Jolly Good Fellow, Shine on, Harvest Moon,* and *For Me and My Gal.* He scratched his head and screwed up his face in an attempt to recall the songs.

"Nope. Reckon not. 'Course, Ah never been to one a them musical shows neither. Guess that's why."

It made little difference. By the time he'd gone through his repertoire of "homemade songs," we'd arrived at our destination.

"Everybody out of the trucks!" The voice belonged to Captain Caesar Montabalm, on loan from the Air Force Survival School to command these field exercises at Brooks Air Force Base.

We slowly climbed down, stretching and scratching and grumbling, until Captain Montabalm issued his second order.

"DOWN! DOWN! Hit the dirt!"

We all looked at one another in confusion. But the sound of a machine gun snapped us out of our fog and sent us sprawling face first into the red dust of the field. I managed to glance up and saw Captain Montabalm standing spread-legged in the middle of us, the machine gun resting on his hip as he squeezed off rounds. He broke out in a loud and boisterous laugh.

"That's the way I like to see you. On the ground. Only next time try wiggling your hips a little to make a little dent in the ground. Some of you have rear ends sticking up so high the enemy would have a field day shooting them off." He laughed again and strutted away toward a clump of trees at the far end of the field. Just beyond the trees stood a high, sloping hill that undoubtedly would play a part in our three days. Hills always play a part in all military operations.

Suddenly we were all very tired. But we dragged our bags from the trucks and followed Captain Montabalm toward the trees. We were almost there when the captain looked up at the sky, wheeled around, and shouted, "Enemy aircraft at nine hundred. HIT THE DIRT!"

We hit it. Hard.

"All clear," Montabalm yelled. It might have been clear to him, but everything was red and fuzzy for us. We were covered with thick red dust. It was in our eyes, in our mouths, ears, noses, throats, and all inside our fatigues.

"ONWARD!"

We made the trees with no further enemy attack.

Jackie and I had planned to share a tent for the three days. But Captain Montabalm had already made out a tent-mate list. Jackie was to share a tent with Carla, and I was with Ginger. It provided the first humorous moment of the day.

"Y'all gonna be my tent-mate, Joni," Ginger bubbled after we'd reached the trees and were all waiting to receive our instructions.

156

"So I heard, Ginger."

"Hope y'all don't snore—tee-hee."

"No. But I walk in my sleep and do some strange things."

"Oh, my."

The first order of business was the erecting of tents in the treed area. Ginger proved herself to be a proficient and hard-working sidewalk superintendent. She stood by and made suggestions as I struggled with the ropes and the canvas. Finally, after having ended up on the ground when the rope I was pulling broke, I looked up at Ginger and said, "Would it be asking too much, Ginger, to have you shut your big sexy mouth and replace it with some sweat and muscle?"

She was stunned. She muttered something about ladies not speaking that way where she came from, but it had its effect. She grabbed hold of a rope, and we soon had the tent up and standing. Not that it was securely erected, but it would provide some semblance of cover for the two of us. We stood back and admired our work. We even smiled at each other ... and watched the tent slowly fade to one side and collapse. I'd tied the ropes too tight on my side, and they'd yanked the tent over.

"Well, let's try again, Ginger," I said with a resigned sigh.

But Ginger had a better idea. She looked around and spotted the med-tech who'd kept her warm in the truck.

"Yoo-hoo," she called to him, a dazzling smile coming to her face, her chest pushed out against the fatigue front. He came running. And he put up our tent for us.

Later Captain Montabalm came around to inspect and complimented us on how nicely we'd done. Ginger assured him that we were fully aware of the necessity of learning and doing right in these matters.

"... after all, Captain Montabalm, it could be the real thing someday."

He liked the spirit. He told us so and swatted his thigh with his swagger stick for emphasis.

"He's kinda sexy in a Spanish way, don't y'all think, Joni?" Ginger asked after he went on to another tent.

"*Si.*"

"What's that mean?"

"It means yes in Spanish, Ginger."

"Oh, that's good. I certainly want to rememba that for when I speak with the captain again."

"I'm glad I could be of help, Ginger. And *no* means no in Spanish, the same as it does in English."

"Well, I'm glad to know that, too, Joni, though I don't think I'd ever be sayin' no to a captain."

Sometimes you just had to like Ginger.

We cooked breakfast there in the trees. It was Air Force issue canned goods, and awful. We ate it fast, cleaned up, and went on to the first exercise of the day. The purpose of this exercise was to simulate a battlefield and evacuate the casualties to waiting helicopters. There were no real helicopters, but we made believe they were up on top of the hill.

A portion of the class was assigned to play patient roles again, and the rest of us had to undertake the evacuation. Roles assigned, equipment broken out and ready for us, Captain Montabalm looked at his watch and held his hand high in the air.

". . . four, three, two, one . . . COMMENCE!"

He started shooting the machine gun as we loaded patients on stretchers and headed for the hill. Ginger had managed to get her attraction of the moment, the warming, tent-building med-tech, as our patient. He was supposed to have received serious shrapnel wounds in the stomach and was given blood by IV. Naturally, we didn't really stick the needle into him. But the plasma bottle was hung on its traveling pole and off we went, the stretcher being borne by the guitar-strumming airman and one other, a skinny little guy with glasses and a very feminine way of speaking. We hurried through the trees and came to the base of the hill. As we looked up, it seemed endless.

"Move on, move on!" Montabalm shouted.

"Psycho," our feminine med-tech mumbled under his breath.

"For-waaaaard!"

"Neanderthal."

We pushed forward. The sun was up now, and hot. Very hot. Mosquitoes buzzed all around us, attacking at will. Once, our feminine friend swatted at one and let go of the stretcher. Down went the patient, dragging the guitar player with him. The guitar player got up, and they lifted the stretcher. Our gay friend dropped his end again, and everyone fell down once more.

"What's going on back there?" Montabalm yelled.

"Injured med-tech, injured med-tech," the faggy airman yelled.

"Injured med-tech, injured med-tech," Montabalm echoed. The word went up the line and soon another med-tech appeared on the scene.

"Symptoms? Symptoms?"

"I think I have a hernia," the fag moaned.

"HERNIA!"

"Hernia . . . down hill."

"No time. MOVE ON!" That was Montabalm.

The med-tech who'd come down the hill looked at me and Ginger.

"One of you will have to pick up the stretcher and move along."

"What about him?" we asked, looking down at the gay airman.

"We'll leave him behind. Captain's orders. Can't jeopardize the unit for one man. Let's go." He scrambled back up the hill.

Ginger and I looked at each other. We pointed at each other. But our patient on the stretcher decided it for us. He took Ginger's hand, squeezed it, and looked into her eyes.

"I don't know if I can make it all the way, ma'am. Hold my hand, please. Like Mom would."

"MOVE IT! MOVE IT!" Montabalm was really screaming now from up on the hillside.

"Hold his hand, Mom," I told Ginger. "And remember you owe me one."

I lifted the stretcher along with the guitar player and we began the ascent up the hill. Every step was agony. Of course, the physical training at basic did prove its worth at a time like this. I found I could manage to carry my end.

Ginger walked alongside the stretcher, holding the patient's hand. Occasionally she'd check the IV bottle and tube for effect.

"My gut, ma'am. It hurts real bad."

"Momma will fix," Ginger would coo and run her hand inside his shirt and massage his belly.

"Bless you, lady in white, bless you."

I thought I might get airsick.

We reached the top of the hill at noon. Midday. Blazing sun. Red dust. Many tears, mostly mine.

"HIT THE DIRT!"

It was easy this time. We simply fell down, allowing stretchers and patients to fall with us.

"NEVER DROP A PATIENT!"

Montabalm strutted around the fallen unit, looking closely at patients, studying their conditions, scowling at nurses and med-techs, and beating the living daylights out of his thigh.

"CHOW!"

"Isn't that sweet?" Ginger purred. "Givin' us an Eyetalian word of greetin' like that when we're so tired an' all. And him bein' Spanish, too."

She stood up and yelled, *"Si,"* to Montabalm.

He didn't hear her.

We had lunch. At one o'clock Captain Montabalm got to his feet and pointed down the hill.

"Ready to move out!"

We struggled to our feet. I pointed to Ginger and then pointed to the end of the stretcher. Our patient, who'd spent the lunch break telling slightly naughty stories to Ginger, pleaded with her to stay by his side. But I stood firm.

"You carry down, Ginger," I said.

"NURSES WILL MAN THE STRETCHERS!" Montabalm was standing in an heroic pose above us, on the hill's crest. I decided not to take this lying down. I strode up to him and told him I'd already carried a stretcher *up* the hill.

"War demands much of us, Lieutenant. Give and you shall be rewarded.

"MOVE ON!"

I went back, picked up the end of the stretcher, and, together with Ginger, proceeded to stumble down the hill.

We eventually made the base camp. A briefing was immediately held to discuss the problems of the first exercise. They were legion, according to Captain Caesar Montabalm. We would have a similar exercise the next day.

But this day wasn't over yet. We had to prepare and eat dinner, secure the camp from enemy attack, and map plans for the next day's assault on the hill.

Securing the camp from the enemy meant posting guards. I was chosen for the first shift. Jackie knew what had happened with the stretcher-carrying and offered to replace me on the guard duty so I could catch some sleep. But I declined her offer.

"War demands much of us, Jackie. I'll be rewarded." She looked at me strangely.

"You OK, Joni?"

"Perfectly, Jackie. Ready, willing, and able."

"Well, just yell if you need me."

I smiled at my friend. "You're a sweetheart, Jackie. And thanks."

Darkness fell on our little outpost, and soon everyone had retired to their respective tents for some much-needed rest. I was assigned to guard the perimeter of the camp at the base of the hill.

"We don't expect you to shoot anybody," we were told before assuming our positions. "But your quick recognition of the enemy and warning can bring men in time to stave off attack and possible destruction of all of us. Look keen, smell well, and never, never let down."

I sat down under a tree and tried to see something up the hill. But there was nothing to see except the black void of the slope against a rapidly darkening Texas night sky.

I hummed to myself. "All mah morals are behind me ..."

A noise. The enemy?

A rock falling.

A bird.

People spitting?

Rain. It started to rain. Great big drops that plopped on my nose and on the ground all around me. I pulled my fatigue jacket up around my neck and stood up. The rain was coming harder now, and I could feel the red earth below turning into a slightly slimy texture. More rain fell, and it was muddy—red mud.

I checked my watch. I had until midnight on my watch. It was only nine-thirty. And then I heard the footsteps behind me. I wheeled around and clenched my fists.

"Halt ... I mean ... halt!"

The footsteps came closer. Just as I was about to scream for help, Jackie appeared from behind the nearest tree and came up to me.

"Jackie, don't ever sneak up on me like that."

"Sorry, Joni, but I asked Captain Montabalm if I could relieve you, and he said I could provided I tested your reactions and watchfulness. He said to sneak up on you. So I did."

"But I told you I didn't want to be relieved."

"I know. And I don't care. Come on, Joni, go on back to the tent and get some sleep. You can pay me back in kind sometime. OK."

"You're sure Montabalm said it was OK?"

"Absolutely. He gave me a lecture on how war brings people closer together. Wars make buddies. Did you know that?"

"I kind of figured it did, watching Ginger."

I agreed to take Jackie up on her offer. I left her there and went back toward my tent, or at least toward where I thought it was. After tripping over stretchers and tent poles, I came upon what I was sure was my tent. I'd gotten down

161

on my hands and knees and prepared to crawl into the tent opening when the giggling inside stopped me.

"Oh, Charlie, I've never done it in a sleepin' bag, although I did go once with a very avid campin' fella."

"Yeah. God, you're built."

"I guess I was fortunate in that regard. Do y'all like 'em?"

"Yeah, Beauty. Beauty. You ready, baby?"

"Oh, my, y'all bet I am."

I sat there in the mud and rain listening to my tent-mate make love with our patient. At least I thought it was our patient. I didn't know what to do. I'd roomed before with girls who had affairs, and it was the rule that the other person would stay away from the apartment while any love-making was going on. I decided the same rule would apply to tents, too.

But I started to shiver in the rain. That's when I decided to go to Jackie's tent and sleep there, at least until she returned from the guard duty shift. Then Ginger would probably be finished and I could go home to my own tent.

I crept along the ground until I came to the tent Jackie was sharing with Carla. I listened. There was only the faint sound of Carla snoring inside. I crawled through the tent flap, climbed into Jackie's sleeping bag, and soon was of another dreamy, warmer world.

In the meantime Jackie had huddled herself up in her poncho and sat gloomily under the tree at the base of the hill. She kept snapping herself awake, but soon a deep drowsiness overcame her and she slumped against the tree trunk. She'd been asleep for maybe twenty minutes when she sensed that someone was nearby. She came slowly awake and sat there half between what was probably a dream and the reality of the cold, wet night. She slowly opened her eyes, and a pair of boots came into focus.

She sat with her eyes riveted to the boots. They didn't move. And then, without looking up, Jackie lunged from her sitting position and tackled the boots ... or the ankles connected to them. The body went down with a heavy thud in the mud.

"Help! Help!" Jackie started yelling as she hung on to the ankles. A pair of hands grasped Jackie's neck and started to squeeze.

"Let me go," a man's voice said.

Jackie bit the man's leg. The man yelled and squeezed her neck harder.

Her screams for help soon brought two or three med-techs

162

to the tree. They reached down and dragged Jackie and her opponent apart.

"Captain Montabalm?" she asked weakly.

"*Si.*" He was covered with red mud. His dark Latin eyes blazed through the red muck, and his voice quivered with emotion.

"I thought he was the enemy," Jackie said, her voice quivering worse than Montabalm's.

"I am, Lieutenant. From now on I am your enemy. DISMISSED!" He tried to execute a perfect about-face but slipped in the mud and fell down. Jackie offered her hand to him, but he ignored it, got up on his own, and sloshed away.

Jackie stuck out the guard shift, was relieved by a med-tech, and wearily went back to her tent. She came inside and gasped when she felt a body in her sleeping bag—mine.

"Joni. What are you doing here?"

I could barely hear her.

"Go away," I moaned. "Go away."

Jackie didn't argue. She left her tent and went to mine. She crawled inside, took notice of Ginger sleeping soundly, and reached to pull back my sleeping bag top. Her hand came to rest on a scruffy, bristly chin.

"Eeeeeek!"

"What? What?" The man in my sleeping bag jumped up and tore from the tent. Ginger woke up, looked over at Jackie, and asked what she was doing in her tent.

"What was *he* doing here?" Jackie retaliated.

"Who?"

"That . . . that . . . that man."

"Oh, my. Musta been Charlie. I told him not to stay. Oh, my." She wrung her hands and apologized profusely.

"Oh, forget it, Ginger. Just shut up and let me go to sleep." She crawled into my sleeping bag and was soon asleep.

The next morning the camp was filled with a tension that was unmistakable. We received a stern lecture from Captain Montabalm on vigilance during watch. Jackie looked at the ground during the entire talk. Charlie, our patient and Ginger's tent-mate the night before, sat there with a serene smile on his face. Ginger watched Captain Montabalm intently, with only an occasional sly smile at Charlie.

We attacked the mountain again. It was no longer a hill. We did it better this time. In fact, we were back at base camp by four in the afternoon. We all washed in our helmets, each taking a turn within our tents for privacy. Ginger went first in our tent and took forever. I was ready to barge in and push her out when she came running out holding a towel across her naked breasts.

"There's a peepin' Tom. There's a peepin' Tom."

Sure enough. The guitar player came scurrying around from the rear of the tent and ran toward the hill.

"That's him," Ginger shouted. "He was peepin' on me."

The guitar player just kept running.

"Seize that man!" Captain Montabalm ordered. Two med-techs raced after him and scurried up the hill in pursuit. Montabalm turned to Ginger. "Now, Lieutenant, tell me what happened."

Ginger started to explain how she was washing in the tent and had just dried her chest and was about to talcum when ...

"Talcum what, Lieutenant?"

"Oh, my. These. I mean ..."

"Put some clothes on, Lieutenant."

"Boooooo." It was a chorus.

Ginger went back inside the tent and returned fully dressed. The two med-techs had caught up with the guitar player and dragged him down the hill. They brought him to Captain Montabalm. The guitar player stood there, his lips pouted and his eyes shifting back and forth between the captain and Ginger.

"Did you peep on this woman, Airman?" the captain asked.

"Golly, no, sir, Ah sure didn't."

"That's a lie," Ginger snapped.

" 'Tain't."

I couldn't resist it.

"Sir," I said, "may I have a moment with you?"

Captain Montabalm reluctantly agreed. He told everyone to hold their positions while we walked away from the group.

"What is it, Lieuteneant?"

"Well, sir, it's just that this airman couldn't be guilty. We were together for the past hour singing songs."

"You sure of that, Lieutenant?"

"Oh, yes, sir. You see, sir, there's more to it. Ginger ... Lieutenant Whip ... is an old friend of mine. A lovely girl and obviously very pretty and well-endowed."

"I haven't noticed. There's little time for that kind of thing in war, Lieutenant."

"Yes, sir. Well, as I was saying, Ginger many times thinks men are peeping in on her. We went through this all the time in basic. Just one of those little quirks of hers. Do you understand?"

He pondered it for a few minutes and agreed that my testimony would prove that Ginger was wrong in her accusation. He strode back to the group, dismissed the guitar player, told Ginger he was confident there was a mistake, and let it drop.

Inside the tent, Ginger was furious with me.

"What y'all tell him, Joni?"

"I told him that with someone as beautiful and well-built as you are, Ginger, you really had to be understanding of a young boy wanting to see that beauty. That's what I told him."

Ginger suppressed a tiny smile, wiggled her head around a few times, and kicked the ground with her toe. "I guess ya can't really blame the fella. He's just a boy and all. Kinda cute, too, I guess."

The three days went by very quickly. Strangely enough, we were kind of sorry to see it end. Adversity breeds companionship, and we all became fast friends as we fought together to win the three-day war. Ginger and Charlie didn't get together again, at least not while I was in the tent. He didn't even put his arm around her during the truck ride back to Brooks.

But the guitar player did have his final moment of musical glory. Jackie asked him if he'd written any tunes while in the field. He said he had and, after much encouragement, sang it for us.

(To the tune of *She'll Be Comin' Round the Mountain*)

"Oh, we carried all them stretchers up the hill,
Oh, we carried all them stretchers up the hill,
Yes, we carried all them stretchers
And broke our backs, you bettcha
Yeah, we carried all them stretchers up the hill."

Everyone broke into a round of applause for his performance. And then some of the other med-techs started egging him on to play and sing the other verse. He turned beet-red and looked sheepishly at Ginger.

"Shucks, Ah can't rightly sing it with women here. 'Specially you, Lieutenant Whip."

"Come on, play. Don't be bashful."

"OK, but Ah reckon you better understand Ah don't mean no offense, Lieutenant."

Ginger agreed she wouldn't be mad.

"The captain whipped us up the hills like mules,
And off we went to battle jus' like fools,
And Ginger leads the way, how that bosom it does sway,
And all us guys jus' march along and drool."

"Tee-hee." Ginger adopted a shocked expression. But Jackie jumped in with praise for our favorite fellow student.
"What a wonderful honor, Ginger, to be immortalized in song like that."
Ginger beamed.
"Why, thank you, young man."
The guitar player winked.
And we all rolled merrily home to base.

Chapter 17

"*Just Think of Me as Your Father*"

General Jeremiah "Wings" Dipman commanded one of the bases at which we were stationed after Flight Nursing School. General Dipman was in the Air Training Command (ATC) and had built his reputation on the Korean War. Legend has it that he was severely wounded during an air strike but, in the face of ever-increasing odds, inspired his men to go back and do further battle.

"Fly this one for the dipper, boys," he is reported to have said from his hospital stretcher. They did. General Dipman, then a colonel, was promoted to general. And his proved inspirational record led him into the training command.

We met General Dipman at the usual reception at his home. He seemed a pleasant man, rather small and chubby, with flaming red hair and a lot of freckles.

"Welcome to my home," he told us with a broad grin.

"Pleased to be here, sir."

"Nurses. Angels, that's what you all are," he said. "I'll never forget the nurses in Korea. Pulled me through, they did. I think they knew more than the doctors." We didn't argue. It was often true.

We met the general at various other times, always social occasions, and he was extremely likable. His wife, a shade taller than General Dipman, was not as pleasant. In fact, she was downright nasty at times. We found that out during a party at the Officers' Club. Jackie and I had excused ourselves from our dates and headed for the ladies' room. As usual, a long line had formed outside the room. We all stood around chatting, waiting for our turn to come up. It soon reached the point where Jackie and I were next to the lavatory. Two other girls came out. We'd started to enter when General Dipman's wife rudely pushed in front of us, gave us a phony smile, and walked right in, leaving us with bad tempers and crossed legs.

"Who the hell does she think she is?" Jackie hissed through clenched teeth.

"I'll be damned," I added.

After finally gaining access to the lavatory and returning to our tables, we both complained to the others with us about the general's wife.

"Oh, you'll get to know about Dipman's old lady," a female captain in personnel told us. "She believes in rank having its privilege at all times, even where the john is concerned." That seemed ridiculous to us, but the captain at our table went further.

"She's technically right, you know. You can pull rank at

168

any time in the service. Of course, nobody would think of doing it in a ladies' room line. Well, except wives like Mrs. Dipman."

We liked General Dipman. And we started to feel sorry for him after that night. His wife was obviously the driving force behind him—such a driving force that it was embarrassing at times. General Dipman was careful never to offend her.

Wings Dipman seemed to have a genuine affection for young officers in the Air Force. He often hosted small informal luncheons for various officers; we were pleased to be invited to two of those luncheons during our first three months on the base. Mrs. Dipman, of course, attended most of them with her husband, which dropped a rather heavy black crepe over the affairs. You simply expected to see her at all the luncheons.

That's why we were surprised at her absence at the third such luncheon held by General Dipman. He'd invited Jackie, me, and two other nurses from the base hospital. Lunch was pleasant and the conversation centered mostly around the need of the Air Force for bright young officers to choose it as a career.

"How would you like to accompany me on a trip?" he asked us over coffee.

We all agreed we'd like that.

"As you all know," he explained, "I'm especially interested in young officers. Well, we have what we call Career Motivation options open to ranking officers. Basically, it involves taking promising new officers on permissive TDY to further encourage them to make the Air Force a career. And I can't think of a more promising group than our young nurses. How about it?"

It sounded marvelous. We all asked the obvious questions of when it would take place and where we would be going on this trip.

General Dipman smiled. "Well, I thought we'd go to Miami. I'm sure you're all as tired of this cold weather as I am. Miami's nice this time of year."

"Wonderful," we said.

"Now. About when the trip would take place. I'd like to leave tomorrow morning. Does that pose any problems for any of you?"

We all voiced our surprise at such last-minute notice. Could we get ready that fast? How would our superiors react? *Why?*

169

"If you can pack your bags, the rest of the problems are solved," he answered us. "I've already arranged with your commanders to fill in for you during the week we're away. The reason I want to go so fast," he continued, "is that I gained my reputation for fast action and thinking. It's something you'll learn as you progress in the Air Force. Decide what's good for your people and *act*. Don't waste time debating with yourself. Make your decisions and act on them. That's how I got my nickname, Wings. During Korea. The odds were great. I was near death. But I looked up at those young flying officers under my command and told them, 'Fly this one for the dipper, boys.' They did and we won the battle. I would have gone back myself if I could have gotten off that stretcher and stopped the bleeding long enough. After the mission one of the boys said I was born with wings. Wings Dipman. I've been proud to be known by that name ever since."

We all reacted appropriately.

"OK then?" the general asked as we left the table. "0700 tomorrow morning. You'll have your orders this afternoon. You'll have a ball, believe me."

Jackie and I packed that night. It was all very thrilling to be traveling as special guests of a general. It was also pleasant to think of a week in the warm climate of Miami.

"The only thing I don't like," Jackie said as we packed, "is that we'll have to spend time with that witch of a wife of his."

I hadn't thought of Mrs. Dipman. The thought, once introduced, was difficult to take. "Maybe she won't come," I said.

"She'll come," Jackie answered. "Bet you a buck."

I took the bet.

We sat around drinking coffee later that night with some of the girls in the BOQ, most of whom were openly envious of our special treatment. The subject of Mrs. Dipman came up, and we were discussing that aspect of the trip when one of the middle-shift nurses came into the room. She'd just left the hospital.

"What's new at the funny farm?" I asked.

"Not a hell of a lot," she answered, kicking off her shoes and flopping in a chair. "Except for Mrs. Wings Dipman. The general checked her in tonight for a week's series of tests. She's pulling rank all over the place, and I'd like to perform a frontal lobotomy on her. What a bitchy woman."

"Pay up," I told Jackie.

"Bet's off," she came back. "Being in the hospital changes things."

I didn't press my best friend. It certainly did change things, especially for General Dipman. He began to appear less a Milquetoast than originally thought, at least in my eyes. It seemed obvious he scheduled everything to coincide with his wife's hospitalization. I mentioned this to Jackie.

"Don't be so catty," she told me. "I'm sure this thing with his wife was unexpected. I'll bet that down deep General Dipman loves his wife, regardless of how bitchy she is."

"It must be a very deep love, Jackie."

The four of us left the BOQ together the next morning and went to flight operations. General Dipman was already there. He was wearing a fighter pilot flight suit, a piss cutter cap set jauntily on his head.

"Good morning, girls," he announced loudly. "The bird's all set to fly, and we'll be off in about fifteen minutes."

"Are you flying us, General?" I asked.

"Not officially. Major Robbins over there is in command. But I'll fly co-pilot for the major. Good to get back in the harness again."

General Dipman really didn't look like he belonged in a pilot's suit. But that's the price we pay for watching too many World War II movies. They all don't look like Clark Gable.

"You girls all look ready for battle," General Dipman quipped in reference to our flight fatigues. We did look like four female jet jockeys in our flight suits and caps. Regulations prohibit female personnel from flying on military aircraft in any other dress than flight suits or fatigues. I think it all boils down to not wanting skirts sliding up to distract flight crews.

The aircraft we were to fly to Miami in was a C-47, the old Gooney Bird of World War II. We climbed aboard, strapped ourselves into the web seats, and waited for Major Robbins and General Dipman to taxi the aircraft out to the runway and take off. We looked out the windows and saw the active runway come into view on the right side. They swung the airplane around and proceeded to approach the runway at right angles. Then we suddenly felt the plane turn all the way around and taxi back to Operations.

"Must be a mechanical," I offered the other girls.

We reached Operations, came to a halt on the apron with engines running, and General Dipman came back through the plane and exited. We watched him run in to Operations.

Soon Major Robbins shut down the engines and came into the rear.

"Sorry, girls, but we're going to have an hour's delay. Might as well get out and grab some coffee."

We did as he suggested. The major joined us, but General Dipman was nowhere to be seen. We assumed some urgent business had arisen for the general to handle. We found out after we returned from our week in Miami just what kind of urgent business had delayed our flight. One of the nurses filled us in on what happened during that hour delay. She was working on the floor when General Dipman came running into the hospital. He was dressed, of course, in his flight suit and looked very concerned. He went right down the hall and entered his wife's room, the only private room in the hospital. Our nurse friend strolled down the hall and stood outside the door, clipboard in her hand and ready to move if anyone came along and questioned her presence there.

"Honey, sweetie," the general was quoted as saying as he went to his wife's bedside.

"Don't honey-sweetie me, you pudgy little bastard," she answered.

"Don't talk that way to me, April."

"I'll talk to you any way I damn well please, you phony cheat!"

"April. Please!"

"Listen, you fat little soldier," his wife said, leaning right into his face for emphasis. "Why didn't you tell me you were taking four nurses on this phony trip of yours?"

"I did tell you, April, pet."

"Yeah. And you told me there were male officers going, too."

"My poor, sweet lovely," General Dipman said soothingly. "Do you think there's anything underhanded about these dedicated young nurses and officers going with your Poppo? Do you think I'd ever try to cheat on you, sweetness?" The eavesdropping nurse supposes the general placed his hand to his head and slumped over the bed at this point. She told us there was silence until Mrs. Dipman spoke again.

"I'll crush your fat skull if I ever catch you playing around, Jeremiah."

"I'd die first, *mon amour.*"

"You bet you will."

"Tell Wings you love him, sexy one." The nurse outside the door thinks General Dipman tried to put his hand on some intimate spot of his wife because she heard a loud smack,

172

and the general said, "You don't have to hit, pussycat. I am your husband."

"That's right. And don't you forget it for one minute. Miami. You phony bastard!"

"I have to ta-ta now, buttercup. You rest and let all the doctors do all their little tests, and I'll be back before you know it."

There was silence. Mrs. Dipman cut off all further dialogue between them, leaving the general to back out of the room, blowing kisses all the way. Our nurse friend had become so engrossed that she wasn't prepared for his exit.

"Thank God he came out backwards," she told us.

"What did he do then?" we asked her.

"He looked very serious and told me he was concerned for his wife's well-being while he was away. He asked that all the nurses try to cheer her up and maybe even play some card games with her."

After the Miami trip we did check on the history of Mrs. Dipman's admission to the hospital. The general had arranged for the tests a week in advance. He'd confirmed the arrangements the morning he asked us to make the Miami trip with him.

General Dipman eventually came back to Operations. We again boarded the Gooney Bird, became airborne, and winged toward Miami. The general invited each of us up front, and we even took the controls for a few moments. It was all very thrilling, especially for Roberta, one of the nurses on the trip. Roberta was a large, languid girl with droopy eyes and with what the male officers on the base termed the sexiest mouth in town. We often looked closely at Roberta to try to gain a better understanding of what the men were talking about. Her mouth looked like any other mouth to us, but that's what's so wonderful about the sexes being different. If men like things about women, that's the way it should be and without question.

"I feel so sorry for General Dipman," Roberta told us after she'd returned from the cockpit and her turn at the controls. "He's so ... so ... well, so alone, it seems, even though he's married. That awful woman. She treats him terribly."

We all agreed, of course.

"Sometimes I just want to take his head and cradle it to my bosom," Roberta added. "Comfort him like a little lost puppy dog."

We said we understood, although it seemed she was carrying things a bit too far.

The flight was long and bumpy. We arrived in Miami that evening, headed for one of the big hotels in Miami Beach, and checked in. We received a lot of strange looks from the well-dressed men and women in the lobby.

"Must be a fraternity initiation," I heard one man say to his female companion, a dazzling blonde of perhaps twenty. He was pushing seventy and possessed a permanent tan.

"The fleet's in," another man of sixty-five said to his girl, a tall, buxom brunette of maybe eighteen.

"Looks like we've got a fly-in hooker convention," a heavyset man with gray hair muttered to a redhead with an hourglass figure, a gown cut low in front and back, and a hand full of diamonds.

"Oh, Mr. Maltrose," she cooed, "you say the funniest things. I told my mother you were so sophisticated."

Jackie and I watched the lobby parade with great interest. "Isn't it wonderful the way all these fathers take their daughters on vacation with them," Jackie told General Dipman. He seemed about to protest her observation but gave it up. Wings Dipman was a gentle man.

The rooms were luxurious in a grossly rococo way. Each had a terrace overlooking the Atlantic Ocean and the expanse of beach between the hotel and the water.

"This must cost a fortune," I said as Jackie and I stood on the terrace.

"Don't worry," Jackie answered. "The taxpayers can afford it." I'd never thought of who was paying for this motivational trip. For some silly reason I assumed Wings Dipman had dug deep in his pocket and footed the bill.

We went back into the room, unpacked, showered, and prepared to join the group for dinner in the hotel's dining room. I was putting a finishing touch to my hair when I noticed Jackie in the mirror. She was peeking around the corner of the sliding glass doors. I got up and started toward her, but she held me back with a wave of her hand. I tiptoed the rest of the way and joined her. Together we peeked over to the next balcony. Standing on it was General Jeremiah Wings Dipman. He was dressed in a very sporty yellow jacket, maroon slacks, perforated shoes, blue shirt, and yellow and pink flamingo tie. His hair was combed a different way and looked much better than the way he usually wore it. He stood bouncing up and down on his toes, a very large grin across his face. Finally, looking up at Miami's proverbial

174

moon-over, he raised his hands in offering and exclaimed, "Oh, god of freedom, Wings Dipman is yours for a week!"

Dinner was a joyous occasion. Major Robbins ate with us but excused himself right after dessert.

"I've got to see a cousin of mine. Lives in Miami. Haven't seen her in years."

General Dipman winked at me and poured more wine for everyone.

"Cousin, huh? Ho, ho. That's an old one, huh? Ho, ho, ho." Then he turned solemn. "Well, let him find some fun and freedom while he can. We only get one shot at this old life. You girls ever think of that?"

"All the time, sir," Roberta answered. She looked into the general's eye and blinked slowly in understanding.

"Yup," he continued. "One shot at it and it's all over. Finis. Cinched. Closed. Think about that. You only get one chance to enjoy life. Don't waste a minute of it."

General Dipman gave each of us a slow and deliberate look, apparently to judge reactions to his philosophy. Jackie seemed nervous and laughed—an inappropriate reaction. I looked down at the table. Betty Kolvin, the fourth nurse on the trip, smiled and tried to look pleasant. But Roberta rubbed her lips together, lowered her eyes, brought them up again, and nodded ever so slightly to Wings Dipman. He nodded back and poured more wine.

It was eleven o'clock when General Dipman slapped his hands on the table and announced, "Well, let's leave this pleasant spa and go on into the night. A little pub-crawling will do us all good."

All of us were exhausted, but it didn't seem prudent and even human to refuse to join our gracious host. He signed the check, tipped handsomely, and led us out of the hotel. A cab pulled up and we all piled in.

"Where the action is, my good man, and don't spare the horses."

The cabdriver drove off. I was sitting up front and heard him mutter, "Don't spare the horses. Another stiff. With four broads yet."

The cabbie dropped us on a corner somewhere in Miami Beach. A few nightclubs glared at us, their neon signs flashing and twitching in welcome. A burlesque house stood lonely on one corner. Some local pubs sat nestled between stores, and an all-night laundromat was filled with people, most of them young women in slacks.

"Well," General Dipman commented, "it looks like our

driver has chosen a less-than-sophisticated part of town for us to visit. But that's OK, isn't it? The other side of the tracks. See how they live."

We walked into the nearest club. It was one of those places where you have a choice of entering one of three rooms, each carrying with it its own admission fee. General Dipman chose the Jungle Lounge room, paid our fees, and we all pushed through lengths of rope hanging from the ceiling. A waitress in a plastic bra and panties showed us to a booth that was shaped like a tree house. We gave our order to the waitress and sat back to adjust our eyes to the room's darkness and see what was going on around us. For my money, and Jackie's, it would have been just as well if we'd remained sightless.

The booths around us were occupied, for the most part, by men and women in various stages of undress and lovemaking. The girls were obviously professionals. They also lined the bar, drinking colored water and allowing the men to make disgusting fools of themselves as they pawed and petted and occasionally fell off the bar stools.

That was all bad enough, but soon a drummer gave out with a monstrous roll and a saxophone player screeched and the floor show was on.

"Ladies and gentlemen, the Jungle Lounge is proud to present Pythonya, the Viper Woman."

A Jewish gentleman in the next booth said to the girl climbing all over him, "The viper voman? Vat does she vipe?"

Bilge-green lights illuminated the small stage over the bar, and Pythonya appeared through a curtain. She was a small girl with long raven-black hair. She wore only the briefest of G-strings, her breasts naked and swaying as the drummer and saxophonist engaged in a brutal rendition of *The Anniversary Waltz*—with a tom-tom beat. But what was most interesting was the long snake wrapped around Pythonya's neck.

"I think I'm going to be sick," Jackie said as she got up and headed for the door.

"I'll go with her," I said.

"Well, we'll all get out of here," General Dipman growled. He paid the bill, cast one last plaintive look at Pythonya, who was kissing the snake, and joined us out on the sidewalk.

"Pretty dull, huh?" he asked as he hailed another cab.

"I just don't like love scenes with girls and snakes," Betty Kolvin said.

"Me either," I added for emphasis.

176

"Well, let's cross the tracks and see the better half," General Dipman said. We found a cab and were driven to our own hotel on the water. The sign out front promised a Lido-type revue in the hotel's main entertainment room. The general said we'd try it.

"Do they have snakes at the Lido?" Betty asked.

"No," Wings answered. "Just some slimy fellows hanging around." We chuckled appropriately and entered the hotel.

The revue was big and brassy with beautiful girls in minimum dress parading through elaborate settings. It was truly an impressive show, but it was getting very late and both Jackie and I were exhausted. After all, the day had begun early.

"Would you excuse us, sir?" we asked the general. "We're both about to fall on the floor."

General Dipman was obviously disappointed but acted graciously and wished us a good night's sleep. Betty Kolvin decided at the last moment to join us, and we left Roberta and the general at the table.

"I'm glad Roberta's staying," Betty said as we rode the gold elevator up to our floor. "I'd hate to think of everyone leaving the general flat."

We agreed.

But we'd no sooner entered Betty and Roberta's room for a few last words before going to bed when Roberta came in.

"Where's General Dipman?" we asked.

"In his room, I guess. He was paged for a phone call and said he'd probably be on the phone for a long time. So I said I'd call it a night and we split up."

"Probably that bitchy wife calling him," Jackie said.

"At this hour in the morning?"

"Why not? She'll probably call him every hour just to keep him awake and make him suffer for taking the trip."

"I feel very sorry for General Dipman," Roberta said sadly.

"I think we all do," I said.

We all went to bed and fell asleep quickly. Next door General Dipman was pleading with his wife to stop yelling at him on the phone.

"I'm up this late because I couldn't sleep," he told her.

"Well, I couldn't sleep either, you coward. You left me to die in this hospital while you gallivant off with those whores."

"April, puddin', they are not whores. They are nurses and officers in the United States Air Force."

"And so are you, you bum."

"Besides, April, you're not dying in the hospital. You're just having a few tests."

"How do you know I'm not dying? How would you know, sitting there in Miami?"

"Yes, love."

April Dipman hung up with a loud bang. General Dipman slowly undressed, slipped into brand-new black silk pajamas, and went out on his terrace. He looked up at the same moon with which he'd started the evening and said, "God of freedom, be patient."

Everyone slept late the next morning. We had brunch at eleven and spent the day swimming in the surf. General Dipman was pleasant enough. But he was obviously distracted by every bikini-clad girl who wandered past our little blanket group. We kidded him occasionally about his wandering eye, but despite his forced laughter, we felt he really didn't like such kidding. We refrained and contented ourselves with soaking up the sun.

We had cocktails at six, and General Dipman presented us with what he termed his Master Plan for Fun.

"I believe in taking advantage of every minute of every day," he told us. "So I've mapped out a sort of schedule for the rest of this week. Is that all right with everyone?"

It really wasn't all right. The thought of a schedule to keep on our week away from military routine was less than satisfactory. But who were we to complain?

General Dipman read off the schedule. There would be swimming, horse racing, jai alai games, sailing, nightclubbing, sauna baths, miniature golf, horseshoes, bowling, tennis, golf, and other assorted activities. General Wings Dipman had slipped into the role of elder camp director.

He finished reading the list of events and then added at the end with a sly glance at each of us, "I'd also like to spend some time alone with each of you to get to know you better and to give you some insight into this Air Force that needs you as career officers." An uncomfortable silence fell over the group as we reacted in varying ways to his shy and almost pathetic pitch for our companionship. General Dipman had started to explain his motives further when a bellhop came to the table and informed him there was a long-distance telephone call for him. He blushed, laughed it off as some "damn official business," and left the table to take the call in his room.

"April?"

"Who else, Wings?"

178

"Well, hi, sweetums."

"Where were you?"

"Oh, having some pineapple juice with ... with Major Robbins."

"Where are those so-called nurses?"

"Oh, off somewhere, I guess. Haven't seen them all day. You know those young people, love. Go, go, go all the time. That's what I like about young officers, April honey. They ..."

"Don't give me that routine again, Wings Dipman. You don't like young officers. You like young *stuff!*"

"April!"

"You come home here tonight, you over-the-hill Romeo."

"I can't come home tonight, snookums. You know that. Daddy has to carry out this assignment."

"What assignment? I hate you."

April hung up.

The general came back to our table and told us he had a bad headache and would beg off for the rest of the evening.

"I think I'll just relax in my room," he said. "I'll probably be up until midnight thinking about all these damn pressing problems you get stuck with as a general officer. Please feel free to stop up and have a nightcap with me at any time."

No one committed herself. But we all felt a pang of pity for General Wings Dipman. I began to sense my own motherly urges coming out strong—head-to-my-bosom and stroking-brow kind of thing.

We decided not to venture out into Miami Beach's nighttime offerings; another drink, shower, and early to bed seemed the choice of all four girls. Jackie and I got comfortable and were watching an old movie on TV when we noticed the shadow flash across our terrace. It went from left to right, possibly from Roberta and Betty's room toward the general's room.

"What was that?" Jackie gasped.

"I don't know. A person."

"A burglar. A rapist."

We sat up in our beds and shook. But the fear didn't last very long. The shadowy figure again crossed the terrace outside our window, this time from right to left.

"Go see, Joni," Jackie said.

"You go."

"No, you."

"Oh, all right."

I moved carefully toward the window and tried to see

through the curtains. Everything was vague and fuzzy. I parted the curtains a crack and looked through the opening. The terrace was clear. I opened the sliding doors and poked my head through. There was nothing—no one.

"Maybe we should call the manager," Jackie suggested.

"I don't think so, Jackie. Why cause trouble?"

We put out the light and talked until we both finally dropped off.

The next day was a round of activities as planned by the general's master schedule. We returned to the hotel in a state of collapse. After showering and changing, we all met in the cocktail lounge. We were in the middle of our first drink when a man approached the table, extended his hand to General Dipman, and exclaimed, "Wings, you old bastard. Oops, sorry, ladies."

The general got up and shook the man's hand.

"Flaps Flugman. I'll be damned."

They did a lot of back-slapping and laughing, and Mr. Flugman joined us at the table. The general introduced him as an old Korean War flying buddy, now Colonel Flugman. The general seemed sincerely thrilled to see his old pal, and they had the gayest time recollecting and recounting past glories. Colonel Flugman made a few dirty-laugh references to the general's harem, and we all giggled and the general laughed. But he never denied the implied meaning of the colonel's remarks. We didn't mind. It was good to see the general so happy.

The men's talk got around to business, and General Dipman mentioned some things in his briefcase he'd like to show Colonel Flugman.

"They're up in the room, Flaps," he told him. "I'll only be a minute."

"Don't bother, General Dipman," Jackie said. "I'll get your briefcase. Just give me the key."

General Dipman protested, but Jackie was persuasive. The general gave her his room key, and she and I went to his room. We walked in, picked his briefcase off the floor, and were walking out when the telephone rang. Jackie went to answer it, but I stopped her.

"You shouldn't answer his phone, Jackie," I told her.

"But what if it's important, Joni? The Pentagon or something."

"You're right. Go ahead."

Jackie picked up the phone.

"Hello?"

I could hear the female voice screeching through the phone as Jackie held it far from her ear.

"What'll I do?" she pleaded.

"Hang up!"

We got out of the room, on the elevator, without saying anything. I knew the caller was Mrs. Dipman. Jackie didn't have to tell me that.

We went back into the lounge and joined the group, both of us with extremely heavy hearts.

We all had dinner together, including Flaps Flugman and Major Robbins, who rejoined us after apparent success in locating his cousin. After dinner we went to another hotel where there was a band for dancing. I ended up with General Dipman on the dance floor and felt it was probably a good time to bring up the subject of the phone call.

"General," I said.

"Call me Wings, Lieutenant. And I'll call you Joni, if it's all right with you. At least for the rest of the trip." He was quite drunk as he spun me around the floor. "You're a marvelous dancer, Joni," he told me. "But I knew you would be the minute I saw you in your bathing suit." He seemed embarrassed in saying this. I simply thanked him for the compliment. The phone call was still on my mind.

"General," I tried again.

"I think we make a good-looking couple, don't you agree, Lieute—er—Joni?"

"Oh, yes, sir."

A cha-cha. The floor filled up.

"General, there's something I . . ."

"Wings, Joni."

"OK. Wings, when Jackie and I were in your room, the phone rang."

He didn't seem to hear me. He was too busy winking at Flaps Flugman, who was crushing Betty Kolvin in a bear hug next to us.

"Not bad for an old man, huh, Flaps?"

Flaps just grunted in reply. He, too, was busy—kissing Betty on the neck and swaying against her.

"Wings," I snapped, "please listen to me. It's very important . . . for both of us."

Wings Dipman looked me deep in the eyes, and I could almost detect a tear.

"I know, Joni. I know. We'll consummate it later."

I stopped dancing and made him stop.

181

"General Dipman, Jackie answered the phone when it rang in your room."

Something started to come through to the general. He blinked a few times and turned slightly gray.

"Yes? Yes?"

"It was your wife."

"April?"

"I'm afraid so, sir."

"Oh, boy. Jeez. Oh, boy."

"Would you like to leave, sir?"

"Oh, yes. I guess." He let out a long whistle.

"I'll come with you, sir."

"Nonononono. Not with me. Nonononono. Goodnight."

General Dipman left immediately. He didn't even say goodbye to Flaps or Major Robbins or anyone else.

"Is he sick?" Flaps asked me.

"He's going to be," I answered.

We assume General Dipman called his wife that night because we were on the plane the next morning at eight.

"I can't even leave the base for one week without some crisis," he mumbled as he boarded the Gooney Bird.

"I certainly don't envy you, sir," Jackie said.

"Nor do I," Betty concurred.

"It takes such great strength to be a general," Roberta said.

General Dipman straightened up on his way through to the cockpit, turned back to Roberta, and said, "Yes, it does. It sure as hell does take strength. Major, cancel the flight plan. We're staying out the week here."

We all went back to the hotel, took different rooms, and played out our week of career motivation. To our knowledge, General Dipman never called home once, and he managed to parry whatever his wife said in her phone calls to him. He lived his freedom to the hilt, with the help of Roberta, who literally cradled his head to her bosom the last two nights of our stay.

"Think what you will of me," she told us, "but that man needed the warmth and companionship of a real woman. And let me assure you Wings Dipman is all man."

It was interesting to Jackie and me how we reacted to the general's brief and desperate affair with Roberta. We expressed some reservation over the incident but agreed during a lengthy bull session that we, too, had felt a desire to indulge General Dipman. We had little contact with him after returning to the base. When we did see him, he appeared to be more relaxed and in command of things, even, to some small degree, of his marriage. All in all, the trip to Miami had proved to be a worthwhile venture and expenditure for the United States Air Force. It didn't motivate us to remain in the service, but it did a world of good for one of its needy generals.

Chapter 18

"The Hospital . . . Our Home Away from Home"

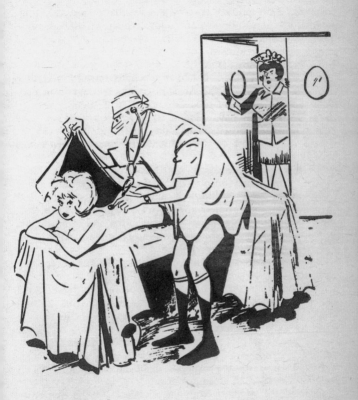

Nurses and hospitals go together. After all, a nurse has to have someplace to practice her trade, hang her hat, and have lunch. A hospital fills this need quite nicely, and in a surprising number of cases proves to be a marvelous place for sick people to visit and utilize in the pursuit of health.

But it must be remembered that a military hospital differs drastically from a civilian installation. The desired end result, of course, is identical: to provide a place where professional people can make you better. It's been our experience that medical care is pretty much on a par at military and civilian hospitals. Each military hospital has its quacks and its incompetents, just as you find in all major civilian hospitals. Certain military hospitals are lacking in equipment for advanced diagnosis and treatment, but so are many civilian facilities. But in reality this lack of equipment or even specialists proves to be less of a problem in the military than in civilian life. It is the policy of the Armed Services that every member shall receive necessary medical care. If a particular hospital on a base doesn't have needed equipment or personnel, the patient will be airlifted to a facility that does. All of this, of course, at no cost to the patient. It's one of his fringe benefits.

We must admit, however, that all the jokes about military medical care aren't unfounded. Sick call, the routine clinic operation on every military installation, often provides less than adequate attention and care for the patient. Then, too, the very nature of the military organization and mind throws up certain roadblocks for efficient and effective medical care.

RHIP—Rank Has Its Privilege.

This age-old and vital part of military life has never been compatible with top-notch hospital care. True, it exists in civilian hospitals also. The very rich or famous tend to get better and more courteous care when confined. But, by and large, everyone admitted to a civilian hospital benefits equally from its facilities. Not so in the military. In cases of life or death—yes. Everyone's life is the same in the Armed Services.

But it's the routine aspects of hospital life into which RHIP sticks its head and interferes.

Perhaps the greatest example of this is in the maternity wards of military hospitals. As we've pointed out, rank is worn not only by its owner but by his wife, and even children at times. Some wives don't wear their husbands' rank. God bless them.

But Mrs. Dennis Brine did. She was married to Major

Brine, special assistant to the commanding general of the base. And many a wife of a young lieutenant fell afoul of Mrs. Brine at a wives' club gathering or command tea. She was so conscious of rank that it was considered dangerous to disagree even on matters of baby care or interior decorating with her.

Lieutenant's wife: "Oh, but I like Kelly green and navy together."

Mrs. Brine: "My dear, you're wrong."

Colonel's wife: "I think it's rather nice."

Mrs. Brine: "Of course. I adore it."

Major Dennis Brine made Mrs. Brine pregnant for the fourth time. Eventually, as it will happen, nine months passed and Mrs. Brine was delivered to the hospital late one night by Major Brine. As he was leaving and Mrs. Brine was being wheeled into the delivery room, she grasped her husband's hand and said firmly, "Make the nurses know who you are and who I am, Dennis. They're liable to think I'm just another officer's wife."

Major Brine did as he was told. He went up to every nurse he saw, introduced himself, told them his wife was delivering, and ended with, "I may not be able to get here too often. As special assistant to the general, I'm tied up a great deal. But I'll get here as often as possible, and I imagine the old man will be over, too. Keep an eye out for him."

We all decided Major Brine was a monumental bore. But we should have met his wife before passing judgment. Compared to her, he was the original nice old man.

She came out of delivery screaming that she wanted to see the hospital commander, Major Jones.

"But, Mrs. Brine, it's three o'clock in the morning."

"I know what time it is, and I also know my husband was commissioned before Jones was. Get him."

Major Jones answered the phone, listened to the nurse, cursed a little, and hung up. He came in the following morning and was met with an impassioned plea from two nurses—Jackie and me.

"Sir, we hate to sound out of line, but could you talk to Mrs. Brine? She's been giving us a hard time ever since we came on duty this morning and . . ."

He held up his hand and nodded in understanding. "I know, I know. I was called about it at three this morning."

Major Jones went to see Mrs. Brine, and she really reamed him out. He listened patiently, agreeing with everything she said. He told us kiddingly that we shouldn't worry about her and said we should treat her as we would any other patient.

That rule prevailed for six hours.

Then the general called on behalf of Major Brine and told Major Jones in no uncertain terms that he'd better see to it that Mrs. Brine received better care. Evidently she'd talked to her husband, who transmitted her thoughts.

Major Jones buckled. And we went crazy. Not a minute went by that Mrs. Brine didn't want something or wasn't complaining about something else.

The most pressing complaint she had was about the room. She insisted upon having one of the two private rooms available in the hospital. These were usually reserved for the general and his family. Naturally, she was given one of them after another call from the general, this time via his secretary.

Once ensconced in a private room, Mrs. Brine really started yelling for service above and beyond what any patient should receive. She even insisted that Jackie read the morning paper to her.

"Dennis does every morning," she told her.

"And I don't," was Jackie's reply.

Jackie was called into Major Jones's office after he'd received a complaint from Mrs. Brine.

"Look, I don't expect you to read anything to her, but please try to hold your tongue. She'll be here only another two days at the most. Try to be patient."

Jackie agreed, on behalf of the entire nursing staff, that patience would be practiced at all cost. But she never considered that the cost would go so high.

We had a genuine emergency that night. Two airmen's wives, both very advanced in pregnancy, were in an automobile accident just off the base as they returned from a movie. They were rushed into the hospital, doctors were summoned, and the whole hospital waited as the staff exercised all its skill to save the mothers and unborn babies.

Fortunately, things worked out for everyone concerned. One baby was delivered, and the mother was saved. The other mother did all right, too, and it was felt that her baby would go full term and remain unharmed.

Everyone collapsed once the crucial work and the tension were over. And Mrs. Brine started yelling again.

"I'm cold."

"I'm hot."

"I want another sleeping pill."

"I'd like my bed changed now."

We tried to hold to the pledge Jackie had made to Major Jones. But Mrs. Brine kept it up and kept it up.

Finally she screamed at Jackie because she was delayed in bringing her some fruit juice.

"Ma'am," Jackie told her, "I didn't bring your fruit juice right away because I was changing the IV for a woman who just gave birth despite the fact that she has two broken legs and a brain concussion."

Mrs. Brine seemed honestly sorry.

"I'm sorry. I didn't realize that. Who is the woman?"

"Mrs. Carter."

"Carter? Carter? I don't seem to know her. Which unit does her husband command?"

"He doesn't command any unit. Her husband is an Airman Third Class and he works in the Motor Pool."

Her mood changed.

"Well, now really, Nurse! I'm sure Mrs. Carter is quite used to waiting for things. At least she'll have to get used to it if she's to be an effective Air Force wife."

I have to admit that Jackie lost her cool. She dropped the tray and the juice right on Mrs. Brine's bed.

"You dummy!" Mrs. Brine screamed. "Get me Major Jones."

"Get him yourself." Jackie left the room.

Mrs. Brine raised enough ruckus to be heard in Washington. Major Jones was forced to conduct an investigation into Mrs. Brine's charges against Jackie, as painful as the procedure was to him.

Naturally, all charges were proved unfounded and untrue. In that particular instance Mrs. Brine had been shut up, and quite officially so.

But it didn't change her. We saw her often when she brought the kids in for treatment, and she remained as obnoxious and rank-conscious as ever, maybe even more so. We all tried our best to avoid her, and usually succeeded.

We soon forgot about Mrs. Brine and just looked the other way when she came in. This could well be the end of the story except for one thing that happened a few months later.

The Air Force was in the midst of one of its many economy drives, and that meant the riffing of officers. Under this system, officers who had been passed up for promotion a certain number of times would be demoted to the highest non-commissioned rank they ever held. In Major Brine's case, he'd been a staff sergeant before becoming a commissioned officer.

Mrs. Brine was an entirely different woman when she next came into the hospital. She haltingly and with a pronouncedly embarrassed look on her face filled out the mandatory form requesting medical treatment. It includes a space for the husband's name and rank. She didn't seem quite sure how to spell "sergeant."

We almost felt sorry for her. But sympathy just wouldn't come. No one deserved the comedown more, and no one would find it a more bitter pill to swallow.

The free and easy access to medical care in the Armed Forces breeds quite a bit of hypochondria. Imagine your favorite hypochondriac with a full staff of doctors and nurses at his beck and call, day and night, and all absolutely without charge. It's like an alcoholic in a wine cellar. Or Ginger Whip in a football team's dressing room. Or . . . Oh, well.

We've seen many hypochondriacs during our military nursing careers, but none to equal Sergeant Wallace Maddox.

Wally, as everyone at the hospital affectionately called him, managed to visit us at least three times each week. Unlike other hypochondriacs who can drive you crazy and make themselves totally obnoxious and bothersome, Wally was a likable sort and truly believed he was inflicted with every disease known to mankind. And he wasn't looking for a soft shoulder to cry on, like most hypochondriacs. Wally wanted to be cured. He wanted that desperately.

The first morning I met him was when he came in to have his recurring numbness checked.

"Where are you numb, Sergeant?" I asked.

"Everywhere, ma'am."

"Everywhere?"

"Just about. Well, except my nose and left ear."

"I see. Well, we'll have the doctor take a look at you in just a few minutes."

"Thank you, ma'am. Say, would it bother anyone if I sort of jumped up and down while I wait?"

"I guess not. But why?"

"Keeps the blood moving. I figure that's the problem with the numbness. The blood just won't run through the veins and arteries. Jumping up and down might help."

I had to stifle a giggle as I gave my permission. He was still jumping when the doctor came out to see him.

"Hi, Wally. That damn blood stop running again?"

"Yup. Real bad this time, too. Just barely tricklin'."

190

The doctor immediately wrote something on a prescription pad.

"Here you are, Wally. We'd better try a new medication." He handed the slip of paper to the sergeant, who expressed his appreciation and headed for the pharmacy.

"Hell of a nice guy," the doctor told us with a smile. "Nicest hypochondriac I've ever treated."

We saw Wally again two days later. He was limping.

"Gout," he answered when I asked what was wrong. The doctor gave him another prescription.

This went on for weeks.

Finally I asked the doctor what he was prescribing for Wally.

"Sugar pills. What else? As long as I can keep changing the kind of sugar pills, he's happy."

Eventually, of course, the doctor ran out of different-colored sugar pills and Wally lost faith. He stopped coming to the hospital. And then one morning he strolled in with spring in his step and a broad, healthy smile on his face.

"Hi, Wally," we greeted him. "How are things?"

"Couldn't be better. Just great. Doc in?"

We told the doctor Wally was back, and he dropped what he was doing and came out to see his most frequent patient of the past.

"Hey, Wally, you look great."

"Feel great, too, Doc."

"How come?"

Wally laughed. "Got married."

He took note of our quizzical expressions and explained further.

"Yup. Got married, and the little lady told me she didn't want no bleedin' heart hypochondriac hangin' around the house. So I said to myself, I said, 'Wally, there ain't a thing wrong with you.' And you know what? There ain't. Not a damn thing." He beamed, and so did we.

Wally shook hands with the doctor and started to leave. Then he hesitated, turned around, and said painfully, "There is one little thing, Doc, that's botherin' me. Honest. For real."

"What is it, Wally?"

He looked at us, and his expression indicated that he'd rather be alone with the doctor. We walked away.

The doctor told us later what Wally wanted. The doctor asked again what the problem was, and Wally answered, "It's

191

down here, Doc." He pointed to his groin. "Kind of a soreness and stingin' sensation."

The doctor had to keep himself from snickering. He told Wally he thought it would go away in a few weeks and to come back if it didn't. He never showed up again. The hospital did get a Christmas card that year from Wally. It was signed Mr. and Mrs. Wallace Maddox and included a photograph of them in front of their Christmas tree. Mrs. Maddox looked pregnant. It was confirmed a month later when she started seeing one of our obstetricians.

In any hospital the staff doctors create most of the internal interest and gossip. Doctors, as we all know, are also human beings. It comes as a great revelation to most people when they realize this fact and further realize that their doctor is capable of making mistakes, both personal and professional.

Every hospital has a number of doctors having affairs with nurses. This isn't unique to the medical profession. Every company has bosses who have affairs with secretaries and assistants.

But each medical affair takes on a certain glamour that is lacking in other professions. The fact that each participant in the affair knows a great deal about anatomy probably contributes to the glamour and interest. The fact that the participants deal so closely with life and death gives medical affairs a certain tension, not unlike amours between secret agents that seem always to end in brutal disaster.

There was a continuing affair at our hospital between the chief of general surgery and one of the operating room nurses. They were madly in love and used every available moment to be together and make love. It wasn't an easy affair because he was married and had eleven kids. That cut in on their time considerably and often caused the nurse to become grumpy and disgruntled.

Things became very tense for the couple. The surgeon kept searching for new excuses to leave the house and meet his nurse-love. But his wife began to get suspicious and would make phone calls to the hospital when her husband said he had to work late. He always managed to cover up the fact that he wasn't there when she called, but he was smart enough to know he couldn't keep it up much longer.

He discussed it with his mistress and suggested a new course of action.

"Melissa," he told her as they scrubbed up together, "I've got a new idea for how we can be together more. I'll tell my wife I have emergency operations at night. In fact, you can call the house to inform me of the emergency. I'll come here and ... well, we'll do it right here in OR. It's never used at night and who'll know? That way, if my wife calls, I'll be here."

Melissa agreed with the plan, and they decided on the following Wednesday evening. That night, as the doctor sat reading the local paper, the phone rang. His wife answered.

"Mrs. Gillespie? This is Lieutenant Melissa Vamp, operating room nurse at the base. Is Dr. Gillespie there?"

The wife turned the phone over to her husband and watched as he acted out the appropriate reactions to what was being said at the other end.

"Ben, I'm ready for you."

A frown on his face. "Hmmmm, sounds serious. How's his general state of health?"

"My general state of health, Ben baby, is superb. I'm firm and have lots of red blood, but do I ache for you."

"Well, that does sound serious." The doctor was enjoying the little cat-and-mouse game they were playing, his wife's presence in the chair behind him adding to the thrill.

"It is so serious, Ben tiger, that if you don't get here right away and use your scalpel on my incision, I'll leap on the first young doctor I see and tell him it was under orders from you."

"I'll be there right away. Keep the patient comfortable and relaxed." He hung up.

Mrs. Gillespie was annoyed at the intrusion. "Do you really have to go out there now, Ben?"

"Afraid so. Ruptured appendix. I'll have to operate right away."

Dr. Ben Gillespie got to the hospital, checked in at the desk, and told the nurse he would be up on the operating room floor. "I'll be in and out of OR, Nurse, checking on some things. Please don't disturb me unless it's my wife calling or a real medical emergency here in the hospital."

"Yes, sir." The desk nurse laughed to herself. Melissa Vamp had checked in with her an hour before and had told the same story. "Gillespie and Vamp are going at it again," she told another nurse. "In OR." They both giggled and went back to their chores.

It was dark on the OR floor. Gillespie got off the elevator and groped down the hall toward the operating room. He was about to push the door open when a pair of hands covered his eyes from behind.

"Guess who, bad man." Gillespie smiled. He reached behind him and gasped a little when his hands found nothing but skin.

"Melissa, you're naked."

"Mmmmmmmm . . . Isn't it nice?"

Dr. Gillespie didn't pursue the discussion. He just picked up Melissa, kicked open the OR door, and carried her to the operating table. He laid her down and quickly started to undress.

"Aren't you going to scrub up first, Doctor?" she cooed.

"Hell, no. Let the staph come."

Their lovemaking over, they sat up and smoked cigarettes. Outside, the lights of the base filtered into the room, casting irregular patterns on their bodies.

"You know what?" Melissa asked.

"No, and I don't care," he answered. "I'm giddy with power and intellect. I've conceived the perfect scheme for doctors to cheat on their wives. What could be more perfect than this? We even had medical equipment and supplies in case one of us needs them during the course of the evening." He laughed and lighted another cigarette.

Soon Melissa started tracing lines down his back with her finger.

"The patient is ready again, Doctor. Is the doctor ready?"

"A doctor can never get tired, Nurse. Not with his patients depending on him any hour of the day or night."

They started making love again. The transition was about to be made from foreplay to the big moment when the phone in OR rang.

"Let it ring," Melissa begged.

"Don't be ridiculous. The whole plan was for me to be available at the hospital in case my wife called. It might be her."

Dr. Gillespie disentangled himself from Melissa's strong grip and went to the phone.

"Dr. Gillespie speaking."

"Dr. Gillespie, this is Lieutenant Madigan at the front desk. It's your wife."

"My wife? What phone?"

"No phone, sir. She's on her way up to OR. I tried to stop her, but she . . ."

Gillespie hung up with a bang and started biting his nails.

"Come back, Ben lover."

"Shut up. My wife is on her way up here."

"Yaaaaa." Melissa jumped off the table and grabbed for her clothes.

"There's no time for that," Dr. Gillespie said. "Quick. Lie on the table."

Melissa did as she was told. The doctor threw a green surgical sheet over her, kicked the discarded clothing under a cabinet, and quickly slipped into a surgical gown. He flicked on the lights, swung a cart full of surgical instruments around next to the OR table, tied a mask over his face, and frowned just as the outer door to the operating room flew open.

Dr. Gillespie looked up with a perfectly executed snap of his head, glared at Mrs. Gillespie, who was on her way through the inner doors.

"OUT!"

She stopped and backed away, allowing the inner doors to swing shut again. Dr Gillespie worked feverishly under the sheet, which was propped up with a frame used to create a tent over the patient. Beneath it, Melissa Vamp was sweating and looking up at Gillespie.

"Is she still there?" Melissa asked in a hoarse whisper.

"Yes," the doctor answered without moving his lips. "Quiet."

Mrs. Gillespie stood placidly outside the OR doors. It seemed she was there to stay until her husband finished his surgery. Things remained at a standstill for at least five minutes, Mrs. Gillespie standing with arms crossed across her chest, and Dr. Gillespie fiddling around under the sheet. He was breathing more confidently now and allowed his hands to play with Melissa's exposed breasts. It looked like she was going to laugh, though, so he stopped the fooling around. Once, when he grabbed a scalpel from the cart and brought it under the sheet, Melissa let out a tiny gulp that frightened the doctor.

"Quiet!"

It began to dawn on Mrs. Gillespie that it was strange for a surgeon to be operating without anyone else present. No nurse, no med-tech—no one. It dawned on Dr. Gillespie at approximately the same time that his wife might be wondering about that same thing. It also crossed his mind that at some point the operation had to be over and the patient would have to be wheeled out of OR. He considered calling a nurse downstairs and pleading for help and discretion. But he couldn't bring himself to do that. He'd have to carry it off himself.

He made his move. Carefully positioning the surgical sheet over Melissa, he slipped her body off the table and onto a stretcher cart.

"Lie still and don't move a muscle," he said through clenched teeth.

"I'm scared."

"Shut up."

Dr. Gillespie wiped his brow, took a deep breath, and pushed the stretcher toward the OR doors and through the inner set. His wife got out of the way. Her husband didn't even look at her. He just pushed through the outer doors, turned left, and pushed the stretcher up the hall at a record clip. His wife came out and tried to follow him, but she couldn't keep up. He disappeared around a corner.

Mrs. Gillespie got on the elevator and went down to the lobby. She sat and waited until her husband walked off the elevator, went to the desk, and signed out. He looked at his wife, turned, and walked out into the night. She ran after him.

"Oh, Ben, I'm sorry. I ... I thought you were here playing around with one of the nurses. I'm sorry."

Ben Gillespie looked down at his wife and the mother of his eleven children.

"Let's never have it happen again. OK?"

"Yes, darling, yes."

Working in a military hospital presents a nurse with a slightly different case load from what she'd find in a civilian hospital. Again, the availability of free medical care has something to do with it.

Take obesity, for example. The Air Force has always been very high on physical fitness. It's reasonable that they would value good physical health. It helps to be in good shape when you're running around chasing or fleeing from the enemy.

To foster good physical condition, the Air Force has been very severe on its members who allow themselves to gain excess weight and are not able to perform the necessary exercises deemed critical to survival.

But this rigidity doesn't always apply to higher-ranking officers. You can understand this. You take a man with a brilliant war record, advance him both in rank and age, and you end up with an old, heroic, and often obese commanding officer. To put him through a young man's training program would be cruel.

But then again, an officer in charge of men must set an example. He, too, must at least appear reasonably trim and in shape.

So ... that's why every military hospital will find a certain number of older ranking officers admitted for "rest" ... or "complete physical" ... or "for undiagnosed internal ailment."

In reality they're there to lose weight. Just as rich, fat ladies go to health spas to lose weight and firm up, these men come to us.

We starve them. We force them to go to physical therapy where they do the same exercises all the other men are doing out in the field. We make sure they get their rest. And they walk out slimmer, trimmer, and more fit than when they come into the hospital.

Another thing you see more of in a military hospital is venereal disease cases. It seems to be an almost unwritten rule that when a man enters the Armed Forces, he has to get a case of VD to prove something.

Now, the higher brass doesn't like its men coming down with "dread social diseases." That's why they make so many movies to warn new recruits against the evils of sin and dirty women. The movies don't seem to do much good, but who's to say? Even one man spared ...

You can always tell a VD case the minute he walks into the clinic for sick call.

"Name?" we ask.

He gives it.

"Unit?"

He answers.

"What's the problem?"

Dead silence. Feet shuffling. Eyes everywhere but on us. Much throat clearing. Sniffling. False starts.

We know right there and then that this fellow has been across the border or into town and is now experiencing what he feels are the symptoms of venereal dsease.

Many times his buddies have talked him into worrying about it. They've been with him, realize he's a novice in things sexual, and begin a campaign to have him run to the nearest doctor before he goes insane and drools at the mouth and contaminates the entire population.

We don't mean to make light of venereal disease. On the contrary, it's a dread and unfortunate disease that takes far too great a toll. It's just that the poor, frightened, and embarrassed young airmen who come in for a VD check and treatment are so pitiful and scared that you have to laugh. What they don't realize is that nurses couldn't care less. To us, it's just another admission.

"What's the nature of the complaint, Airman?"

"Well, ma'am, I'd like to see the doctor."

"Yes, I know. But you have to tell me first before you see him."

"It's a personal matter, ma'am. Real personal."

"Now come on, Airman, it can't be that personal."

"Believe me, ma'am, it is."

We stand firm.

"You must tell me what the problem is before you see a doctor."

"Well, I was in a gas station the other night and couldn't wait to find a decent and clean men's room, so ... so I had to use it. And I'm afraid it was contaminated."

"I see. Suspected VD," we yell loud enough for all to hear in the waiting room.

He dies. He slinks in to see the doctor.

Actually, we try to be very discreet about those things. We don't think it's at all funny that anyone has VD. We just think it's funny how airmen approach us when they need help.

Every military hospital also has its doctor who's engaged in research of one sort or another. Civilian hospitals are, of course, centers for research. But there's really little need for it in a military installation. Military doctors are there to cure. Research findings are applied, but seldom is research conducted on military grounds.

Still, there is always the doctor determined to make a breakthrough on government time and money. We don't know of any who have succeeded, but Dr. Marcus Monroe, staff pathologist, was determined to make his mark while serving his three-year hitch.

His area of experimentation was the liver and the effect alcohol had upon the liver. It's always been known that the liver is the first to go when someone drinks too heavily. But Dr. Monroe had a notion that it wasn't how much you drank, but rather what you drank. He'd gone beyond the point of simply studying various kinds of alcoholic beverages (vodka, Scotch, bourbon, gin, etc.). He was going as far as to determine what effect various brands and qualities of each type had on the human liver.

"If the world drank Ambassador," he'd rave, "we'd never have another case of cirrhosis."

No one took Dr. Monroe seriously except Dr. Monroe. You had to give him credit for hard work. You'd find him staying night after night in the laboratory, filling beakers with different types and brands of alcoholic beverages. These samples were carefully locked in a tall locker Dr. Monroe had purchased with his own money and placed inside the cubicle he used during the day. It was said that all the world's whiskey was contained in that locker, and many a jestful and sometimes entirely serious plan was hatched to raid Monroe's Distillery.

No one really knew how serious he was until he announced something one day at a general staff meeting.

"I'm proud to announce that I've been asked to present a paper on my research to a regional meeting of pathologists," he told us. "It's being held in Kentucky two weeks from today. I don't wish to sound immodest, but I do hope you all realize how much prestige this will bring to this hospital, each of you, and all Air Force medical personnel around the world."

We applauded and went on to other business.

Dr. Monroe's report was to be highly confidential until he made his formal presentation. No one in the hospital had ever seen it, but a few days later Monroe asked the hospital commanding officer to read it and comment. He reluctantly agreed to do this and, after scanning it late one afternoon, left it on his desk and went home for the night. I was on duty that night and had reason to go into the administrative offices. I couldn't miss it. The binder was bright red, the lettering vivid yellow:

REPORT ON LIVER DETERIORATION BASED UPON INDIVIDUAL BRANDS OF ALCOHOLIC BEVERAGES

By Dr. (Capt.) Marcus Monroe

I picked it up, made a careful mental note of how it had been placed on the desk, and took it with me. I read his report that night, and so did Jackie. It sounded very scientific: how each brand had deteriorated sample cells of human tissue in controlled laboratory conditions. It wouldn't be appropriate or fair for us to list those brands in this book. It wouldn't be right because the report was laughed right out of the pathologists' conference as ridiculous, unscientific, and even pitiful. In fact, Dr. Monroe wasn't even allowed to present his report. He'd sold them on it on the basis of letters he'd written to the committee chairman. Once they received the actual report in advance of Dr. Monroe's arrival, they immediately canceled the invitation.

Dr. Monroe reported on the cancellation at the next monthly staff meeting.

"Gentlemen ... and ladies, I'm extremely sad and dismayed to report to you a situation that is not only frightening to every member of the scientific community but is frightening to every citizen of this country as well. As you all know, I was to speak before a regional conference on my research findings in the field of liver disease and its causes, with stress on specific brands of alcoholic beverages. I regret to inform you that my appearance was canceled. Why? Why, you ask? I'll tell you why. Because the money-hungry distillers of our fair nation worked behind my back and under the table to suppress my findings. Do you know what they did in Kentucky, the state in which the meeting was to be held? They ran newspaper editorials condemning my findings. Why? You ask why? Because Kentucky floats on the revenue from bourbon. That's why. Science has been buried by the crass commercial booze merchants of this country. But I will fight on. I will do this not only in the interest of science and for a better, healthier liver, but in the interest of gaining the recognition deserved by the men of military medicine."

No one really said anything to Dr. Monroe. He was obviously hurt and upset, and to get into a discussion with him would only make things worse. As much as we felt Dr. Monroe was a bit of a nut, we did feel sorry for him and his misdirected efforts. That's why we really didn't like it when some wise guy broke into Dr. Monroe's liquor cabinet and stole all the bottles. They never did find out who did it. We all suspected a shifty-eyed med-tech from Gary, Indiana, but you couldn't accuse him without proof, the proof long gone into somebody's stomach. Dr. Monroe gave up his research project, asked for and received a transfer, and we never heard from him again.

The caliber of Air Force doctors varies greatly. There are a few failures, unfit to treat any human being for any problem. But these are in the distinct minority, just as they are in civilian practice. There are a certain number of mediocre doctors who, knowing they would not fare very well in the competitive world of civilian life, remain in military service where it is secure and routine. However, there are a substantial number of excellent, dedicated doctors.

One of the most dedicated doctors we've ever known was in the Air Force. His dedication was so strong that he went from Airman Third Class to Captain and doctor by studying medicine in his spare time. This particular person is one of many who have benefited from the educational opportunities offered by the Armed Services. Naturally, most men taking advantage of these programs don't strive to become medical doctors. But this one did, and after many years of grueling work, he became a staff doctor. It was quite a day when it all happened. For all those years nurses had been telling him what to do as a med-tech. And suddenly he outranked us and told us what to do. And there wasn't a soul who resented it. It was very heart-warming to see him succeed, and everyone knew he'd make a fine, dedicated career doctor in the United States Air Force. After all, the Air Force had made it all possible.

Every Air Force hospital of any size also has a psychiatrist. They come in all sizes and shapes, all manner of hang-ups, and all pursuing their individual courses of treatment for the same ills.

There was one who seemed to receive some vicarious pleasure in getting patients to talk about sex.

AIRMAN: You see, Doctor, I have this terrible fear of height.

DOCTOR: I see. And what does the height remind you of? A woman?

AIRMAN: What?

DOCTOR: Does the height remind you of a sinful woman waiting to drag you down to your death? Come on, you can tell me.

AIRMAN: Well, no. You see, the height makes me afraid I'll fall and kill myself.

DOCTOR: Tell me, did you have sexual experiences before puberty?

AIRMAN: No. In fact, I graduated before I ever went out with a girl.

DOCTOR: What did you do on that first date?

AIRMAN: Threw up.

DOCTOR: That's incredible. What passion and release!

AIRMAN: Nah. I had too much pizza and beer.

Air Force psychiatrists are always faced with personnel who feel they've made a mistake in joining and now want out. They can't just walk out, but the Air Force doesn't want maladjusted people in its ranks. So the psychiatrist becomes a last resort.

DOCTOR: What's your problem, son?

AIRMAN: I'm in love with the sergeant.

DOCTOR: When did you first notice this feeling?

AIRMAN:	The first moment I laid eyes on him. God, he's virile.
DOCTOR:	Do you think the sergeant loves you, son?
AIRMAN:	No, he won't even give me a second look. I'm about to go ga-ga.
DOCTOR:	How do you think all this will end up?
AIRMAN:	I guess I could start going with his buddy and try to make him jealous.
DOCTOR:	Do you think that will work?
AIRMAN:	I guess not.
DOCTOR:	Do you love me, son?
AIRMAN:	No.
DOCTOR:	Why not?
AIRMAN:	Look, do I have to love everybody who wears a clean shirt? Besides, you're married.

Or:

AIRMAN:	You see, Doctor, I'm God, but nobody believes me.
DOCTOR:	How do you know you're God?
AIRMAN:	The water. The way it all gets out of the way when I come to it.
DOCTOR:	Any other reasons, son?
AIRMAN:	Who needs other reasons? Does the water get out of *your* way?
DOCTOR:	(*Being clever*) Yes, it does.
AIRMAN:	Does anybody believe you?
DOCTOR:	Never. But let's not worry about it. OK?
AIRMAN:	It's fine for you to say that, but it's no help to me. I'm the one who gets wet.
DOCTOR:	(*Senses a breakthrough*) You get wet? When?
AIRMAN:	Whenever it rains. What are you, some kinda God?

We've found military nursing stimulating, enjoyable, and challenging. We've met the nicest people, had the loudest laughs, and never felt more needed. And we should correct any misconceptions you may have at this point. Most of an Air Force nurse's time is spent helping very deserving servicemen get well. As a military nurse, you experience moments of great sadness and moments of great joy. The sadness needs no explanation. That's why we've devoted our book to the less serious aspects of our careers. Dealing with sick and injured people has never been a source of enjoyment for anyone. This is especially true when the injuries and sickness come as a result of a war. But we learned early in the game that a long-faced and sullen nurse never did a thing for a shot-up GI who's frightened and lonely. The ability of the American fighting man to smile through his tears is legend. And his ability to do this should never be counteracted by a nurse who isn't able to smile through hers.

Chapter 19

"Not That Cavity, Doctor!"

It's really the saddest thing that people neglect dentists when they think of the medical profession. Dentists are called Doctor for good reason. They work in vital medical areas of the body, administer anesthesia, operate, extract, medicate, cure, alleviate pain, and confuse patients as well as any other medical doctor. Besides, more military people remember dentist stories than they do doctor stories. That's because dentists are very special people, both professionally and personally.

All dentists are fun-loving. Everyone knows this to be true. And the most fun-loving dentist we ever had the pleasure of working with was Captain Maxwell Margale. Max had a nickname which I learned about, not by working with him, but as a patient.

I settled in his chair after his nurse had taken X-rays, and I gripped the arms of the chair as he began picking at a loose filling.

"Nervous?" he asked with a maddening touch of scorn to his voice.

"Yes. Dentists hurt."

"Not me. Why, in dental school they called me Dancing Fingers."

"Dancing Fingers?"

"Yup. Dancing Fingers Margale. The touch of a diamond cutter."

Dancing Fingers Margale certainly did have a light touch. I first noticed that when he ran his fingers down my chest. He'd taken out the loose filling and had just kneaded some filling material in his fingers. He pressed some of it into my drilled tooth and casually wiped the excess off on the bib that hung down over my chest. It took me a minute to realize what he'd done. I was about to say something when he attacked my mouth again and I was incapable of saying anything.

He worked some more of the filling material into the tooth and again ran his fingers down the bib, this time on the right side, his fingers tracing the contour of my breast.

"Watch it!"

My voice startled him, and he dropped his pick. "What's the matter?" he asked, picking up the pick.

"What you did," I answered. "I mean, you just can't go around . . . fondling girls in your chair."

"Fondling? I beg your pardon."

"Yes, fondling. You just fondled me."

"I did not."

206

"Yes, you did. You . . . fondled me . . . right here." I pointed to my chest.

He turned crimson.

"Here. Right here." I lifted the bib so he could see better. Then I realized how silly that was and turned red myself.

Dancing Fingers Margale rose to full height and looked down his nose at me.

"I was wiping my hands," he said with deliberation. "I'm sorry."

"Well, I am, too. I thought you were trying to get fresh with me."

"I wasn't."

"I know."

"May I start working again?"

"I guess so."

He finished filling the tooth without saying another word. I noticed he was careful to wipe his hands on a towel, although he did make a move toward the bib on a few occasions. Each time he did, he smiled and managed to restrain his hand from making contact.

I came to learn later that this tendency to wipe hands on the patient's bib is a common one among all young dentists. Dancing Fingers was no exception. I suppose he's now enjoying a lucrative practice somewhere on the East Side of Manhattan, capping, drilling, and filling the teeth of the jet set. And I assume he no longer allows his dancing fingers to stray onto his patients' bibs lest he receive a sharp right cross to the jaw from a wealthy matron with overbite.

Dancing Fingers Margale became great friends with Jackie and me. Jackie even worked with him for a week when the dental nurse was ill. Her exposure to the world of dentistry— military dentistry, to boot—has resulted in her becoming a diligent and fanatical teeth brusher.

"They really inspired you?" you might ask her.

"No," she'd answer, "but I just don't want to ever end up in a dental chair."

Poor dentists. They are angels in white when a tooth has abscessed in the middle of the night and you're ready to put your whole head in the oven for relief. They're looked at with deep respect when they've pulled all the bad, old teeth and refitted you with gorgeous new ones. And when your gums are bleeding, and every bite of food brings agony to your mouth, and to smile at a friend is painful, and your breath is bad without doubt, the friendly dentist is there to soothe your gums, sweeten your breath, and assure you it

207

isn't a manifestation of some latent venereal disease. Bless him at these moments.

But nobody loves a dentist. And that's probably why dentists laugh a lot when they work on you. They want and need to be loved. They want you to enjoy and savor their fingers in your mouth, the cotton soaking up every last drop of saliva, the clamps digging into your gums, the drill's steady drone, and the cold air hitting the nerve. It isn't easy to love a dentist, no matter how much they laugh.

Dancing Fingers Margale worked with a team of young dentists at our base. And they were under the wing of Major Karl de Sade.

Major de Sade was a pleasant enough man. But every young dentist hated him. The reason was simple. The younger men were restricted to drilling and filling caries. Major de Sade took care of all the more interesting and challenging jobs like root canals and capping and extractions. He was a zealot in reserving these tasks for himself. Obviously, morale was low in the dental wing of the hospital.

"I'd sell my soul for one root canal," a young dentist told Jackie during a coffee break.

"Me, too," his buddy chimed in. "Or one post-and-crown."

The young dentists, led by Dancing Fingers Margale, went to Major de Sade with their grievance. They told him they wanted to perform some of the more difficult procedures of their profession.

"Gentlemen," the major told them, "you have a great deal to learn about military dentistry. Rank does have its privilege, you know. Soon many of you will become majors, and then root canals and post-and-crowns will be yours. I've waited fifteen years for my rank and its privileges, and you must wait, too."

"But, Major de Sade, many of us will be going into civilian practice within a few years. We need the training now."

De Sade slammed his fist on his desk and glared at the men before him.

"Just as I thought. Disgusting. You want to use taxpayer money to train you for some civilian practice where you'll become rich and fat and useless. No, I say."

He wouldn't bend. And things got desperate. Finally one young dentist, Captain Rasch, could tolerate it no longer. He got very drunk one night at the Officers' Club and made his decision.

"Tomorrow," he mumbled to himself, "I shall have me a root canal."

The next morning Captain Rasch's first patient was a gangling airman with a toothache.

"First toothache I ever had in my life, Captain," the airman said as Captain Rasch prepared to examine the tooth.

Rasch looked inside the airman's mouth. He'd never seen such a perfect set of teeth. They were brilliant white, perfectly formed and aligned. Rasch ground his teeth as his conscience fought with his madness. The airman noticed the wild look in his eyes.

"Somethin' real bad, Captain? I never had any trouble with my teeth before."

"Could be, Airman. Could be." He was committed. The airman's trouble was a single carie in a lower molar, obviously the result of its hard-to-reach location when brushing. A moment's drilling, simple filling, and all would be well.

But Rasch was beyond the point of reason. Major de Sade's militancy had pushed Rasch over the brink; he would do the root canal.

"Looks like a root canal job," he told the airman as he wiped the sweat from his brow and glanced sideways to avoid the airman's reaction.

"Woweeee," the airman gulped. "You sure?"

"Well, we'll take an X-ray and confirm it. But I've done a lot of these, and this looks like a clear-cut root canal case to me. Just a simple one, though. You're lucky you caught it in time."

The airman was thankful. And Rasch went right to work. Normally, any patient who looked as if he or she needed anything beyond simple filling was referred to Major de Sade. But Rasch was confident he could get away with this attempt. He went out and informed Jackie he'd need her help.

"For a filling?" she asked as she came back with him into his treatment room.

"A root canal!" He tried to say it casually and without fanfare. But his quivering voice was at odds with his intentions.

"A root canal? You?"

The airman heard and sat up straight.

Rasch thought quickly.

"Yes, me. Everyone else is busy and I'll do it. I know I shouldn't be doing these simple things, but I'll help out."

Jackie smiled and understood.

Rasch drilled out the tooth and extracted the nerve. He

held it up to the light, and his eyes filled up. The airman, numb from the Novocain, strained to see better.

"There it is, Airman," Rasch said with great pride. "A nerve. The canal is now open. I'll begin treatment."

Jackie made an excuse to leave as Captain Rasch set about gouging out the root canal with the various thin files, inserting cotton strands and smelling them after removal for sign of infectious odor, taking X-rays after each step to insure things were well down in the canal, and, in general, performing all the ritual and procedure of a full root canal job. Rasch finally packed the canal, placed a temporary filling in the tooth, and instructed the airman to come back the following week. The airman seemed pleased and relieved that Rasch had discovered the "need" for the root canal work, and left the office with a wide although understandably glaciated grin.

Captain Rasch called Jackie back into the office the moment the airman left.

"Jackie," he told her, "I know I can trust you. I'd never have attempted the root canal if Craig were here." Craig was the sick nurse. "But you won't tell De Sade, will you?"

Jackie promised she wouldn't tell anyone of his daring decision to buck the system.

Of course, Nurse Craig did come back and was on hand when the airman arrived for his second session with Captain Rasch. He managed to avoid her as he slipped the airman into the chair and feverishly went to work on the second root canal session.

Rasch managed to hide his illicit activities until the fourth and final session with the airman. He was shaping the final and permanent filling when Nurse Craig came into his room and asked if she could have the complete file on Airman Tuckerman.

"Unnnaaaaaaah," the airman in the chair went upon hearing his name. He spit out the cotton and sat up.

"Easy, Airman, easy," Rasch told him. He turned to Nurse Craig and asked why she wanted his patient's file.

"Major de Sade's orders, Captain," she answered.

"I'll talk to the major myself," Rasch replied and pushed Airman Tuckerman back into the chair. "Don't ever spit the cotton out again, Airman," he scolded.

"Unnnaaaaaaaah," Tuckerman said as Rasch pushed more cotton into his mouth.

Rasch worked like a man possessed. His work on Tuckerman completed, he sent the airman on his way with the words, "You can be proud of your root canal, Tuckerman. And thank you."

"Unnnaaaaaaaahhh," the airman said as he rubbed his jaw and left the room.

Rasch turned and gazed longingly at neat rows of drill bits arranged in order of size and pain infliction potential. He picked up the one that had burrowed into Tuckerman's slightly decayed tooth and twirled it around. Replacing it, he opened the bottom drawer of the cabinet and carefully removed a tiny white box. Inside, securely wrapped in cotton, was Tuckerman's nerve. Rasch slipped it into his shirt pocket, gathered up Tuckerman's file, and went down the hall to Major de Sade's office. The major greeted Rasch with a smile and a pat on the back.

"Sit down, Bob," the major said. He went to his desk and took out an X-ray folder. He slipped an X-ray plate from the envelope and looked at it against the ceiling light. He handed it to Rasch.

"Take a look, Bob."

Rasch nervously glanced at the X-ray. He knew it well. It was of Airman Tuckerman's root canal, taken while the slender file was in place. It was standard procedure to check the depth of the canal by X-raying a metal file in place.

"Root canal, wouldn't you say, Bob?"

Rasch nodded in agreement.

"Recognize it?"

Rasch gulped. De Sade's eyes had narrowed and taken on a fiery glow.

"Yes, sir. I recognize it. *I did it!*"

"Did what, Rasch?"

"The root canal. On Airman Tuckerman. I did it and I'm glad. I'm glad."

"You realize, of course, Captain Rasch, that any military unit operates on discipline as its basis. It's no different here. This patient's root canal needs should have been referred to me immediately."

Rasch was sweating. But then he realized that De Sade didn't know Tuckerman hadn't really needed a root canal job. All De Sade could be angry about was Rasch's doing the job himself. As far as De Sade knew, Tuckerman really had needed the work.

"I guess I lost my head, sir."

"There's no room for that, Captain Rasch. You can save that kind of thing for your *civilian* practice. But in the

211

meantime I have to punish you. Take it like a man, Rasch. No scenes."

"I'll try, sir."

"Good. I'm putting you on cleaning for one month. Nothing else. You'll clean teeth and that's it. Understand?"

"Yes, sir."

"Dismissed."

Captain Bob Rasch got through the month of cleaning detail. It wasn't easy, but when things became intolerable and he felt he was wallowing in huge vats of tartar and nicotine stains, he had only to take out and fondle Tuckerman's nerve and things would seem better.

Military dentists tend to be clannish. They take great delight in comparing stories of patients, especially female patients. For in the history of dentistry, female dental patients comprise the majority of funny stories.

Things have changed some. With less use of general anesthesia, there are fewer cases of women claiming rape in the chair while under the influence. Those dentists who were stung by such charges soon learned the necessity of having a female nurse present at all times when working on a woman under general anesthesia.

But even with rape charges out of the question, the presence of a female nurse provides a witness of a different kind.

People say funny things when anesthetized. Some become violent and break the straps. Some swear. Some revert to childhood. And some, like a general's wife we knew, act out all their repressed frustrations.

Dancing Fingers Margale did the dental work on Mrs. Wilson, wife of a staff general. She came into the dental office as the mildest, sweetest, frailest, and most frightened little woman we'd ever seen.

But once Dancing Fingers put her under with sodium pentothol for an extraction, she turned into a vamp to end all vamps.

"Love me, Maxie, love me," she groaned, stiffening in the chair and clasping her hands behind her head. "Love me *now!*"

It was quite embarrassing. But then General Max Wilson became a dental patient and was reported to have said under anesthesia, "I'm so tired, I'm so tired. Get off my back."

And the dentists had something to talk about at Happy Hour.

Dentists are great lovers of the practical joke. Jackie found

212

this out during her week in the dental wing when they showed her how to clean dentures in acid in the lab.

"Put 'em in in the morning and take 'em out at night," they told her.

She had one set of dentures to clean one morning and placed them in the acid as directed. But being forgetful at times, Jackie didn't remove them from the acid before leaving for the night. It really didn't make much difference because the acid wouldn't do any harm overnight.

But one of the dentists came in early the next morning, saw the dentures in the acid, and decided to play a little game with Jackie. He removed the dentures and replaced them with a laboratory specimen that consisted of tooth fragments, broken bridge, and pitted molars. Jackie came in, saw them, and let out a shriek.

"Whose dentures were those I cleaned yesterday?" she asked the head nurse.

The nurse had been let in on the game. "Colonel Piedmont's," she answered.

Jackie spent the day alternating between trying to do something with the second set of dentures and practicing her apologies to Colonel Piedmont, whoever he might be.

They let her in on the joke at quitting time.

Of all the dentists we've worked with, Dancing Fingers was the biggest lover of playing jokes on his patients.

Once, after he'd inserted a bite stick in a sergeant's mouth and told him to clamp down on it, he proceeded calmly to light the other end with his cigarette lighter. The sergeant went cross-eyed watching the flame progress toward his mouth.

Dancing Fingers also liked to insert the air hose in his mouth and talk. It had the effect of talking under water while breathing helium. And when he didn't particularly like a patient, or was working on a girl with an especially attractive mouth, he'd have them do tongue exercises for ten minutes while he watched. They'd have to stick out their tongue and draw it back in in rapid cadence. And no one, as far as we know, ever questioned or balked at this nonsense.

The highlight of Jackie's week in dentistry came when Blade Lancer, Hollywood glamour boy and more recently Airman Third Class, came in as a patient. His reputation as a great lover preceded him into military service, but no one really knew whether this reputation was the result of the Hollywood press agents or was based on actual conquests.

Airman Lancer settled in the dental chair and flashed a

213

blinding capped white smile at Jackie. "My friends call me Blade," he said. "What do your friends call you?"

"Lieutenant Sutherland."

"Formal friends, baby. But I could get you in a more informal mood."

"Don't bet on it ... Airman." Jackie could be nasty when called upon.

"Pulling rank, huh? I'll give you something to pull."

Jackie responded by sticking a piece of cardboard into his mouth. "Here, Airman. Bite on this."

"Why?"

"So when I X-ray your pearly mouth we'll see better what's under those caps."

"X-ray? No, thanks."

"Why not?"

"Listen, baby, I know all about X-rays and what they can do to a guy. I'm too young to be a boudoir bore."

Jackie laughed.

"Come on, Airman ..."

"Call me Blade."

"I'd prefer to call you Airman. Now let's get this straight. You don't want an X-ray because you think it's going to affect your potency?"

"You bet your thing, baby. No X-rays."

Jackie decided that to argue would just prolong the time spent with him.

"OK, Blade, I'll make a deal with you."

"Anything, baby, anything. You're the best thing I've seen in uniform since Veronica Lake."

"I didn't mean that kind of deal. Besides, you ought to talk to Joni about Veronica Lake."

"Any time, baby."

"Right. In the meantime my deal is that you let me take the X-rays and I'll rig you up with a lead shield. Guaranteed to keep the rays from straying. OK?"

Blade Lancer agreed with some reluctance. Jackie fetched the lead apron and attached it around his neck like a bib. It reached to his knees as he sat in the chair.

"OK," she said, "let's get the pictures taken." She swung the X-ray machine around and lined up the nose cone with Lancer's cheek. She'd started to leave the room to flick the switch when he sat up, reached up in back, and untied the apron.

"What are you doing?" Jackie asked. But it really didn't have to be explained. Blade Lancer took the lead apron and

214

folded it into several layers of thickness which he placed on his lap.

"I just want to put it where it counts," he said, settling back in position in the chair.

"I'd suggest you shape up, Airman, or I'll put Novocain where it counts." Jackie's words evidently had their fearful effect because Airman Third Class Blade Lancer didn't give her any further trouble.

As we said before, dentists are very special people. Personally, we can't think of a more difficult area of medicine to work in than dentistry. It's so important and yet so frustrating; many dentists suffer frequent periods of dejection because they feel they really don't perform a vital enough function. No life or death. No deathbed consultations. No distraught wife to comfort. No scrubbing up or being paged to emergency wards and the like.

But every one of us knows the feeling of deep gratitude when our dentist makes the pain go away.

Actually, I almost married a dentist. But he had one habit that carried over from his job that drove a wedge between us and caused us to break up.

My dentist really wasn't unique. Many others in his profession have the same habit.

He smelled everything. The habit comes from the root canal procedure, in which they constantly place cotton strands into the canal and, after pulling each one out, smell it for signs of infection. It's a necessary and useful part of the business.

But I'd give my boyfriend a sandwich and he'd pull the bread apart and smell the ingredients.

He'd go to kiss me and I could hear him sniffing my neck.

I couldn't stand it anymore.

Some dentists are grabbers.

Some laugh all the time they're drilling.

And others shake their heads while they're working—a most unsettling experience.

But all in all, dentists are nice people. Nice to visit and fun to live with, sometimes.

Chapter 20

"What's a Nice Girl Like You Doing in a Tent Like This?"

Out of each war emerges a legend of a young, pretty nurse going into the combat zone and returning a year later with one hundred thousand dollars in small bills. Those concerned with preserving the image of the military nurse will argue that these girls became incredibly proficient at cards, dice, or footracing.

Unfortunately, or fortunately for those sex-starved American fighting men in remote areas of the world, such rationalization is not true. The few nurses who have gone the proverbial route of rags to riches in war zones have generally become incredibly proficient at what Barbara Thompson would term "getting laid." And they also learned the value of this proficiency.

The most famous case of battle-zone prostitution by a military nurse occurred with an Army girl (we're not copping out—we've known a couple of Air Force prostitutes also, but they couldn't compare to this particular Army nurse).

Vera Cole was an extremely tiny girl—five feet and weighing about ninety pounds—a graduate of a good nursing school in New York, and a very efficient and hard-working professional.

Vera was assigned to one of the area Army hospitals in South Vietnam and quickly set about healing the wounded, comforting the distressed, and relieving the frustrated. But to accuse her of being a Hardhearted Hannah would be less than fair. It would be more accurate to compare her to that musical comedy heroine who couldn't say "no"—and liked pretty clothes.

Vera got started as a semipro prostitute back in New York. She'd lived a normal life, had her share of dates, and shared her bed with a few of them. But along came Fred to change her life.

"Vera baby," he told her one night as they ate dinner in a small French restaurant, "I've gotta level with you. I've had it with the kiss goodnight. This is our third date already, and all I get is that peck at your door. I need more than that, sweetie. I need SEX!"

"Well, Fred," Vera said as she spooned through the cheese on her soup, "I'm afraid I'm not sexually attracted to you. I mean, you certainly are a pleasant date and I do enjoy your stories about the longshoremen's union, but I just can't find any of the warmth that's so necessary before we go to bed."

They didn't say much more until dessert.

"I'm gonna level with you, Vera. I don't want to see you anymore. I take you out to all these expensive restaurants

218

and nightclubs and I end up ... Well, I don't mind telling you this. I end up calling a prostitute because I'm so hot and bothered."

"That's awful, Fred. How much do you have to pay them?"

"Depends on who I call, Vera. Sometimes twenty-five. Sometimes thirty. Anyway, I'm a physical man, and I guess I'd better find another girl. Nothin' against you, Vera. But I'm a man and I've got needs."

Fred took Vera dancing after dinner, and they returned to her apartment at about midnight.

"Well, one last peck, huh, Vera?"

"Will you be going to a prostitute now, Fred?"

"I don't wanna talk about it."

"Come in with me, Fred."

"You mean it, Vera?"

"Yes, Fred. I mean it."

They entered the apartment and Fred poured himself a glass of ginger ale. He sat down on the couch next to Vera and grabbed her.

"I've gotta have you, Vera," he said as his hands ran all over her.

"You can have me, Fred. You can have me."

Vera got up and slipped out of her dress. Fred sat in rapture as she shucked her slip and, clad in pants and bra, went around turning off most of the lights and placing a Jackie Gleason record on the record player. Fred got up and started undressing.

"Fred," Vera said softly from across the room.

"Yeah, yeah?"

"Would ten dollars be too much, considering dinner and all?"

"Huh? Ten dollars. What ten dollars?"

"For me. I hate to see money going to some dirty prostitute."

"Ten bucks? For you?"

"Yes, Fred. And then in the future you can just give me the twenty-five and not bother about dinner. How would that be?"

Fred was flabbergasted. He rubbed his hands and looked around for someone, but they were alone. He tried to say something two or three times, but nothing would come out. Vera reached behind her and unsnapped her bra. It fell to the floor, and Fred gave out with a reflex whistle of awed appreciation.

"You're not so little ... Hell, Vera ... you're ... I think I only got six bucks left."

"I'll take the six, Fred. And from now on we'll have a more honest relationship. There may even be warmth."

"OK, Vera. But act like we're doin' it because you wanna do it. OK?"

"OK, Fred."

That did it. Fred and Vera made love for an hour. Fred came back again the following week and asked Vera to dinner.

"No, Fred. Just come here and give me the money you would have spent on dinner. Like we agreed."

Fred became a once-a-week visitor at Vera Cole's apartment. And so did William Reed, married advertising executive. Tuesday evening was reserved for Casper Cosset, seventeen-year-old son of the wealthy shipping magnate, Cornelius Cosset. And there were a few others.

For Vera, it all made sense. She still dated boys whom she liked and enjoyed. But the extra money came in handy, and it demanded much less of her time than dating each of her customers. Besides, she preferred a pizza brought in for dinner to a lengthy dinner at a restaurant. An hour spent with Fred or Cornelius or William resulted in twenty-five dollars, less two dollars for the pizza. It was a good deal as far as Vera was concerned.

But Vera became weary of her life for some reason. She decided she needed a change, and the United States Army seemed the kind of change she needed. She joined, went through training, spent six months at an Army hospital in the Washington, D.C., area, and received her orders to Vietnam.

She had been in Vietnam a month when a young captain passing by outside the hospital said, "Hi, spinner." Fred had called her a spinner, and she knew what it meant.

"Hi," she answered back.

They went to bed that night. The following morning the captain kissed Vera good-bye and handed her fifty dollars.

"Here. Buy yourself something pretty next time you're in Saigon."

Vera protested. Then she accepted. And it started all over again, only this time the stakes were a lot bigger.

Vera Cole became the most popular spinner in Southeast Asia.

"Hey, you hear about that nurse back at the base?" a GI would ask another while they were pinned down in some Vietnamese swamp.

"The spinner?"

"Yeah." Two bullets whistle directly over their heads, bringing on an onslaught of invective.

"You ever have her?"

"Nah. Maybe next time back at the base."

"Harry made it with her."

"Yeah? What it cost him?"

"A hundred."

"A hundred? You gotta be kiddin'."

"Nope." A mortar round lands close. "We'll get you, Charlie, you creep."

"Is she worth a hundred?" the other GI asks.

"How long you been here?"

"Eight months."

"Had any lately?"

"Two months ago. In Saigon."

"Any good?"

"Yuk."

"So the spinner is worth a hundred. Right?"

"Yeah, I guess so. She is damn pretty."

"You bet." The unit commander calls for an assault on the Viet Cong position.

"Let's go."

"Wait a minute. She clean? The spinner, I mean. I got a dose from that broad in Saigon."

" 'Course she's clean. She's a nurse, ain't she?"

"Yeah. They know about all that. Hey, wait a minute. She's an officer, ain't she?"

"So what?"

"Well, do you have to call her ma'am and salute and stuff like that?"

"Hell, no. Everybody's the same in the sack. No rank. Come on, stupid. We're missin' the fun."

Meanwhile, back at the base, Vera Cole continued to amass her own personal fortune. Her services were common knowledge among the GIs at the base, and even some of the officers began to frequent Vera's room. One of them, a surly major, tried to bring pressure to bear on Vera.

"Look, Lieutenant," he told her, "I know all about this little operation of yours. I could blow the whistle and see them hang you for hustling, especially with enlisted men involved."

"Look, Major, do you want it or don't you?" Vera had toughened during her months in Vietnam; she didn't need any haggling with anyone, superior officer or not.

"You bet I want it, Lieutenant. Right now. And don't start giving me any prices, because from now on I'm on the house. Right?"

"Wrong, Major. Get out."

"I'll get you, Lieutenant, you . . . you . . . you whore."

The next night Vera was entertaining one of the colonels who'd broken into her ring of admirers. She told him of the major, and he promised to take care of it. One week later Vera stood watching as a new unit shipped out for an extended period of jungle fighting somewhere near the demilitarized zone. Leading the group was the surly major. Vera waved and went back to work in the hospital.

Vera had one steady customer, a private serving in the finance office. He had a master's degree in economics from Harvard and soon became Vera's confidant, adviser, and financial consultant.

"You've got to invest it, Vera," he told her one night over dinner. "You can't just keep putting all this money into the Credit Union. The interest will never keep pace with inflation."

"I know that, Richard. But I just die whenever I think of taking a risk with this money. After all, I've had to give something of myself to make the money. By the way, how much do I have now?"

Richard thought for a moment.

"I don't have the figures with me, Vera, but it's a little over fifteen thousand."

Vera did some thinking.

"That's all? I only have five months to go."

"That's my point, damn it," Richard said. "At the rate of output you're capable of achieving, that should net you about another ten thousand. That's twenty-five thousand all together. Now if you let that money lie in the Credit Union, the most you'll make in interest is twenty-five hundred dollars a year. But in good common stocks you'll not only collect dividends, but the stock appreciates in value. Hell, you could become a wealthy woman if you listen to me."

Vera bit her lip and looked away from Richard.

"But that bothers me so, Richard. I mean here we are fighting a dirty war because there are some bigwigs back home who make a killing on wars. And I'd kind of feel the same way if I made money from their stocks."

Richard roared. "Vera, you *are* making a killing from the war."

"I know, I know. But to invest it in American industry seems ... well, it seems unpatriotic."

"Please, Vera. Let me take your money and invest it for you."

Vera pondered Richard's suggestion for a few days. Finally she told him she was going to let him act as her stockbroker.

"I can't be your stockbroker," he told her. "Not here in Vietnam. But I have a very good friend back home who'll handle the transactions for you. I'll tell him what to buy and sell."

"You'll do this for me, Richard?"

"Sure. I like you. Besides, I admire initiative. It's very Republican. And if you feel a little guilty sometimes, you can get rid of the guilt by being nice to me. Just sometimes. OK?"

The deal was made. Richard arranged for Vera's money to be sent to his friend in the States, who, in turn, followed Richard's suggestions for investment. Soon Richard was able to report to his client that she now owned a portfolio of the following stocks: AT&T, Union Carbide, American Airlines, Du Pont (Vera protested because of napalm, but Richard convinced her all was fair in love and war), Fairchild Hiller, Memorex, IBM, Avon (the Avon lady at the base was a nurse), Xerox, and RCA.

"Solid, huh, Vera?"

"I guess so, Richard. But is it safe?"

"Of course it's safe. The whole world would have to blow up before these stocks would go down the drain."

So Vera continued her moonlighting with all proceeds going to Richard and his friend in the States. It was during her final month in Vietnam that Richard hurriedly took her from her room and led her to behind some cans of gasoline.

"Vera," he whispered, "have I got a deal for you! Jason"— his stockbroker friend in New York—"just contacted me about a sensational opportunity. It's a new company in the rare metals field. And Jason says it'll go from its present price of eighty cents to at least twenty dollars in a month. They've discovered an incredible metals supply and will announce it shortly. If you buy in now, you'll make a killing. Believe me."

"Well, all right, Richard. I'll give you what I make this week and you can send it to Jason."

"No, Vera, no. I want you to take everything you've got in stocks, sell the stocks, and reinvest it in this metals company. And you've got to do it right away."

223

The thought of further risking her hard-earned money was a grim one for Vera Cole. But she had great faith in Richard and his friend Jason.

"All right, Richard," she said. "Go ahead."

Vera took the extra money earned during her last month of duty and spent it on a holiday in Europe before returning to the United States. She arrived in New York and went directly to the office of Jason McGee. Jason's private secretary ushered Vera into his plush offices high atop Manhattan where he sat smoking a cigar and watching a tiny Sony television set.

"Miss Cole. Welcome back," he said, switching off the set. "What can I do for you?"

"Well, since you have all of my money, I'd like to know what's happened to it. Richard had you invest it in some small metals company that he said would do very well. I can't even remember the name of the company. Has it done well, Mr. McGee?"

"Frankly, that company went bankrupt soon after I gave Richard the tip."

"Oh, no!" Vera started weeping as hundreds of nude males paraded before her, each wearing their insignia sewn or pinned to their skin.

"But," Jason McGee continued, rising and punctuating the air with his cigar, "the stock did very well for a short period of time. In fact, it went up to twenty-eight dollars. We took it upon ourselves, with Richard's blessing, to sell it at that figure. We've reinvested the money in solid blue chips again for you."

Vera tried to say something but couldn't. Jason saved her the agony.

"So, having invested twenty-seven thousand dollars in the stock at eighty cents a share, you had thirty-three thousand seven hundred and fifty shares. Selling it at twenty-eight brought you about nine hundred and fifty thousand dollars. You might call yourself a millionaire, Miss Cole."

Vera Cole now owns a nursing home for the elderly somewhere in Indiana. She also owns a new car agency in town, the funeral parlor, two pizza parlors, a drugstore, and the town's weekly newspaper. She never married, and she became a virgin after-the-fact. Her only link with her past came when she received a news release from Mr. B.J. Montrose, Executive Director of a society known as the Southern Society for the Prevention of Deflowering Belles (SSPDSB). It called for an immediate investigation into the military's use of female personnel as prostitutes. Vera never ran the news release. But she did write Mr. Montrose:

Dear Mr. Montrose:

Thank you for your thoughtful and well-written news release on your organization's efforts and programs. I am considering it for publication.

Enclosed please find check in the amount of $500 as my contribution to your work. Your expressed aims are admirable, and I wish you well.

(Miss) Vera Cole
Publisher

Chapter 21

"Moonlight Doesn't Become an Officer"

None of the Armed Forces likes to see its members moonlight—take a second job in their spare time. One of the reasons for this attitude is that in taking a second job, the person involved indicates he isn't paid very much in his first job—that of being an enlisted man or officer in Uncle Sam's military corporation. This thinking has always struck us as slightly silly, since everyone's pay scale in the Armed Forces is public record. Taking a second job doesn't seem to give away anything.

But there's another factor taken into consideration by the military in the moonlighting matter. This has to do with a touchy civilian population, especially when a military man or woman takes a job away from an idle private citizen. We first learned about this from Jimmy, the piano player at the Officers' Club. Jimmy was an Airman First Class, a valued member of the base band, and a very in-demand pianist for playing dates in town.

There was a bandleader in town who was especially high on Jimmy. But after using him on half a dozen jobs, the bandleader, Hugo, was visited by the secretary-treasurer of the local branch of the American Federation of Musicians.

"Hugo, we understand you've been using one of them base fellas on piana. Huh? Huh?"

Hugo smiled and started to defend his actions. But the union representative, a gas station owner and former tuba player named Maynard, leaned in close and really put it to Hugo.

"Huh? Some union member you are, Hugo. Huh? Yeah. Us in the union tryin' all the time to get higher wages and an extra intermission and maybe a sandwich on weddin's, and whatta you do? Huh? Huh? Pull in a scab. A military scab, no less. Huh? And what about Troy? Huh?"

"Troy who?"

"Troy Littlebugger. Huh? You know Troy Littlebugger."

"Troy Littlebugger?" Hugo threw up his hands and shook his head back and forth. "What *about* Troy Littlebugger, Maynard?"

"All them kids. Huh? Payin' dues into this here union for thirty-seven years. What about that, huh?"

"What about that, Maynard?"

"Where was Troy last Saturday night whiles you was playin' that weddin'? Huh? I'll tell ya where he was. He was home with all them kids and his wife. That's where Troy was whiles you was makin' money with that scab piana pumpa."

"Now wait a minute, Maynard." Hugo tried to look serious

228

and responsible. "Troy Littlebugger is the worst piano player in Texas. The worst. The last tune he learned was 'Charleston,' and he screws that all up every time. I can't use him."

"Huh? Can't use him? Since whens you so hot on music? Huh, Hugo? Troy Littlebugger's got pretty good rhythm. I played a job wi' Troy not more 'n two years ago. Played damn good, too. Real solid. Good boogie-woogie. Damn good on the march, too, whens the bride comes in. Don't get drunk, neither."

"He knows six songs, Maynard."

"Six, huh? You say six? That shows how much *you* know. Besides, Troy's a good union payin' member. Ain't fair to have that scab take away work that's rightly Troy's."

Hugo sneered. "I will not use Troy Littlebugger as a piano player on any of my jobs, Maynard."

"That so? Well, lemme ask ya about a couple a weeks ago, Hugo. I heard you went and used a bass fiddle player from the Air Force base. Huh? That right, Hugo? Huh?"

"Yes, I did."

"And he was a nigga, weren't he, Hugo?"

"Yes, he was, Maynard."

"Damn. All that business 'bout bein' born wi' rhythm is a lot of bunk, Hugo. Whata you think we got ourselves a good segregated union here fo'? Huh?"

"I don't know, Maynard."

"Well, that ain't important. The important thing is we got plenty a good bass fiddle players right here in town. No need for you to go gettin' one a them Air Force bebop, drug-takin' fellas."

"What bass players do we have here in town, Maynard?"

"Well, jus' to name one, I'm thinkin' a Charlie Riddy."

"He doesn't even know how to tune a bass, Maynard. Besides, the last time I used Charlie was at a wedding last year. He got drunk and unzipped his fly on the bandstand right in front of the bride."

"Well, now, Charlie told me himself that girl was flirtin' wi' him and was askin' for that. Huh? How about that, Hugo?"

"How about that? He also fell into the wedding cake. How about that, Maynard? Huh? Huh?"

Maynard snorted and delivered his ultimatum.

"From now on, Hugo," he said, "you hafta use union fellas. The only time you can use one a them scabs from the base is if I can't git you one a our boys. Understand?"

"I understand, Maynard."

"OK. Huh?"

"OK, Maynard."

"Ciao, Hugo."

"Ciao?"

"I keep up, too, Hugo. Right? Huh?"

"Right."

Hugo stuck to his word. From that moment forward he would call Maynard at two minutes to nine—two minutes before a playing job starting at nine.

"Maynard? This is Hugo."

"Howdy, Hugo."

"Look, Maynard. I've got a problem. I need a piano player, bass player, and drummer for tonight."

"For tonight? What time's the job?"

"Nine."

"Nine? That's now."

"Right, Maynard."

"Hell, I can't git you no . . ."

"That's what I figured, Maynard. I'm using some of the base boys. *Ciao.*"

And all was well.

There has always been a problem between the military and the civilian population on this matter of moonlighting. The most vivid example of it during our tours of duty came when we were nursing at a base hospital in Massachusetts. One of our fellow nurses was an Irish girl from Boston. She was very cute, a good nurse, and totally involved in every facet of our society's great problems. She had a marvelous gift of gab and would engage you in a heated debate on any subject and at any time.

One night, while sitting around the Officers' Club, our Irish friend, Pegeen O'Hara, was hammering home a point on oil depletion allowances with a young doctor. She'd overwhelmed him with an impressive flow of fact and opinion when he threw up his hands and said, "Pegeen, why waste your time arguing with us one at a time? Get a job on radio."

She did. Quietly she made a date with the station manager of a small independent radio station in the adjoining town. The station was a hobby for the manager, Raymond Massingill, an elderly gentleman with a fairly large bank account and a love of broadcasting. But despite some financial security, too long a period of loss with his radio station could deplete his savings. That's why he reluctantly allowed his disc jockeys, two teen-agers working seven days a week for sixty-five dollars a week, to program the most raucous rock 'n' roll music known to Western man.

"Sorry, Miss O'Hara, but rock 'n' roll is paying the bills. There's no room here for a talk show."

Pegeen had never accepted defeat in anything that could be debated. Two hours later she'd convinced Mr. Massingill to give her one hour each evening during which she would conduct a telephone talk show, with listeners calling in to argue with her.

"I'll have to change my name, though," she told Mr. Massingill. "The Air Force, you know."

He agreed this would be prudent, and Pegeen O'Hara became Doris O'Sheen, with an ad in the local paper to get things going.

"Miss O'Sheen?" the voice asked that first night on the station.

"Yes. What topic would you like to discuss?"

"Sex."

Doris pushed the button cutting the caller off the air. The seven-second delay device did its job, and she went on to the next call. It was a young man with very pointed and vehement views about Vietnam. He was against the war, and so was Doris.

The local American Legion commander called next to present an opposing viewpoint.

"Commies, all of them," he boomed into the phone. "Hippies and yippies and punks being used by the Commies."

Doris went back at him. She cut him up with her head full of facts and her authoritative way of presenting the facts.

While all of this first-nighter excitement was going on, two special people listened with interest. One was General Jimmy Joplin, World War II hero, devoted foe of Communism, and commander of the base in Massachusetts at which we were stationed.

The other listener was Walter Buckles, aging conservative voice of the local political machinery, wit and scholar and frequent guest on the few radio and television talk shows in the area.

General Joplin was on the phone the minute the program came to a conclusion. He called Major Ripples, base intelligence officer. It was Major Ripples' duty to brief General Joplin every morning on world events and trends of interest to the general, the Air Force, and the nation. It was his job to assemble and digest news from every available official and

231

nonofficial source for these high-level briefings. Usually he ended up relying on local newscasts, day-old editions of *The New York Times*, and Huntley-Brinkley.

"Ripples?" the general said.

"Yes, sir." Major Ripples recognized the general's voice immediately.

"Well, what do you think, Ripples? They're here now, right here in this town. And they've taken over the airwaves. What's your reaction?"

Ripples didn't have the slightest notion what the general was talking about. He'd spent his evening washing the kitchen walls, dusting the den furniture, laying tiles in the second bathroom, and nailing boards over the window his son had broken that afternoon. He accomplished all this while his wife conducted a nonstop monologue along the lines of, "All you do is sit all day while I break my back washing and bending and lifting. You sit and solve world problems. You wanna solve a problem? Unclog the downstairs toilet. Intelligence officer. Stupidity officer. Fat and lazy . . ."

Ripples did his tasks and thought a lot. This night he contemplated rat poison. The weekend had found him in a Hitchcock mood; beat her with a frozen leg of lamb, then cook and eat the weapon.

Ripples wasn't about to be taken off guard by his boss, General Joplin. That was his strength as an intelligence officer—he was never caught with his intelligence down.

"Interesting," he answered the general. You couldn't miss with an answer like that.

"You bet it is. Grass-roots America and the Commies are moving in like weeds. That's the way they do it, Ripples. Mix the roots of healthy democracy with the roots of killer weeds. And when we try to spray on some weed killer, those damn liberal bastards turn off the nozzle."

Ripples couldn't imagine what event triggered off the general's tirade. He reviewed in his mind what he'd heard on the radio as he drove home from the base that afternoon. Nothing special.

"So let's do what we're paid to do, Ripples," the general went on, "and check into this O'Sheen broad. O'Sheen. That's Irish, isn't it?"

"Ah, yes. Maybe not, General. You never can tell about those Commies. They change names."

"Good thinking, Rip."

The general hung up. Rip Ripples muttered to his wife about the phone call and the strange name, O'Sheen.

"You dummy," Mrs. Ripples said. "Doris O'Sheen. On the radio. Some intelligence officer. She started tonight doing one of those shows where you call in and discuss things."

"Did she sound Irish, Sophia?"

"No, dummy. She's a Russian, and she's poisoning the water supply." Sophia Ripples went back to television while her husband laid a few more tiles in the bathroom. "Poisoning the water," he muttered to himself as he slopped glue on the floor. "Maybe her coffee in the morning."

While General Joplin talked with Major Ripples, Walter Buckles had Raymond Massingill on the phone.

"You told me, Raymond, that if you ever did a talk show on your station, I'd be the one to do it," Buckles snarled into the phone.

"Yes, yes, yes, Walter," Raymond Massingill answered. "And I changed my mind. This girl is good. Besides, she hasn't gone over any deep ends like you."

"What deep ends?"

"Conservative deep ends. You've become so conservative I'm afraid you'd start calling *me* a Communist on my own radio station."

"Well, we'll see about this, Mr. Raymond Massingill. We'll see. There's nothing worse than an old liberal." He hung up on the amused radio station owner.

Pegeen O'Hara had, of course, no idea her debut as Doris O'Sheen caused such a sensation. The station was flooded with calls, some violently opposed to some of the things Doris stood for on the air and some in agreement with her. But all were a firm indication to Raymond Massingill that the show was a winner. He even received a call from the local druggist who said he wanted to buy advertising time during the program.

Pegeen never let on to any of us back at the base about her newfound radio career. She simply went about her nursing duties, as pleasant as ever. One airman, confined to the hospital after an appendectomy, mentioned having heard the show the night before.

"You should listen, Lieutenant O'Hara," he told Pegeen as she took his pulse. "This girl is great. Her name's Sheen or something like that. Listen tonight."

Pegeen smiled and agreed she would. What a wonderful thing to know someone enjoyed you so much. And how maddening not to be able to reveal your true identity and personally accept the praise.

233

"Oh, well," Pegeen sighed as she went on to the next room.

While Pegeen was making her rounds, General Joplin was in conference with Major Ripples.

"Damn it, Ripples," the general growled as he paced in back of his desk. "I know this isn't any of our official business. I know that already, and I don't need my intelligence officer to tell me that. But you know what? I'm going to make it our business. I'm going to take it upon myself to kill the weeds of Communistic theory while they're still struggling to grow in this town. I want this O'Sheen woman investigated. Do it under cover. Of course, if you or any of your squad are discovered, I'll have to disavow any knowledge of your activities. We can't go upsetting this town, at least not until we've got the goods on the Mata Hari sitting and broadcasting right in their back yards every night." General Joplin slumped back into his chair and covered his eyes with his hand. He slowly rubbed his eyes as he said quietly, "Damn, Rip, but even I get weary protecting our own people from Commie threats right under their own noses. Sometimes I get tired, too."

The local newspaper showed up at the radio station the next morning and wanted an interview and photographs with the town's new broadcasting star, Doris O'Sheen. Mr. Massingill thought quickly.

"She's home preparing for tonight's show," he told them.

"Where's home?"

"Are you crazy? Do you think anyone as controversial as Miss O'Sheen would give out her home address? Not on your life."

The reporter and photographer left the radio station but promised to return that evening to get some pictures of Doris O'Sheen while she was on the air. As soon as they left, Massingill got on the phone and called the number Pegeen had given him. Actually, she'd given him two numbers. This one was the base hospital.

"Yes, sir?" Pegeen responded when Massingill told her who he was.

"Look," he said, "the whole town's talking about the show last night. The newspapers want pictures of you. New sponsors want you to make appearances at their stores. I think one of the TV stations might even be here tonight to get some footage on you."

Pegeen was tongue-tied for the first time in her life. But Mr. Massingill came right back with the answers. He told her

234

he was sending out to the base a friend of his who had a background in makeup in the community theater. Pegeen would change her looks before coming to the station each evening. Her identity could be kept a secret; Massingill was sure of that.

Pegeen wasn't sure about what to do. She wanted very much to continue the radio program. But she didn't want trouble with her superiors in the Air Force. All she'd wanted to do was spend one hour a night arguing important points with many people. She'd never dreamed she'd become important, important enough to be a news figure.

"Do you really think we can keep who I am a secret, Mr. Massingill?"

"Absolutely, Pegeen."

The makeup woman came to Pegeen's BOQ room at dinnertime and gave Pegeen a wig, glasses, nose putty, various skin makeup products, and some instruction in using the materials. She helped Pegeen this first time, led the way to Pegeen's car, making sure no one was around to see her, and bid her farewell and good luck.

Pegeen kept looking at herself in the car's rear-view mirror. She couldn't get over how completely changed the wig and makeup caused her to be. Her confidence began to build, and by the time she arrived in town, she was ready to face all comers. Massingill had cautioned her to park her car some distance from the station to avoid any close inspection of the vehicle. She did as he suggested, surprised to see his wife waiting at the parking lot with her car.

"Hop in, Pegeen," Mrs. Massingill said with a broad smile. "Ray asked me to do this every night. I'm happy to do it."

Everything seemed quiet in front of the tiny building housing the station. But once inside the front entrance, that tranquillity became a thing of the past. There were maybe a dozen people milling around in the small office. One came right up to Pegeen and said, "Miss O'Sheen? I'm Billy Marks from the paper. I'd like to ask you some questions and then get some pictures. OK?"

Raymond Massingill jumped to the rescue.

"Miss O'Sheen goes on the air in fifteen minutes, gentlemen. You can use the next five minutes for photos. I've prepared a full bio on Miss O'Sheen for you. She'll be able to give you five minutes for questions *after* the show. Just have patience."

Someone flicked on some TV lights, strobe lights started flashing in Pegeen's face, and people started yelling instructions to one another and to Pegeen. It seemed to go on for an eternity before Mr. Massingill jumped in and led her away to the safety of the studio that stood just off the office, thick soundproof glass separating the two rooms.

"I'm scared to death, Mr. Massingill," Pegeen told him the moment the door closed, shutting off all sound between the rooms.

"Don't worry about a thing," Maasingill told her. "You read this bio I've made up for you while you're doing the show. Plenty of commercials tonight. You'll have lots of time. Then you just answer their questions after the show based on the bio. OK?"

"OK," Pegeen agreed. "But I don't want them looking through the glass at me during the program."

Massingill went out and draped an old curtain over the glass. The prerecorded tape brought the station up to eight o'clock, another prerecorded tape gave the time, station identification, and the introduction to the *Doris O'Sheen Show*.

The hour went quickly. The callers were interesting and vocal. And Pegeen had a chance to read her bio during hastily recorded commercials for the local druggist:

Doris O'Sheen, one of the most valuable and sought-after properties in the broadcasting world, will be a nightly feature on this station. Born in Florida, educated in New York and Texas, Miss O'Sheen comes to us from California, where she captured the minds and ratings of the Los Angeles area.

Miss O'Sheen feels that the controversial nature of her show demands that a certain veil of secrecy be maintained about much of her private life. Suffice it to say her father was a noted explorer and big-game hunter, her mother a leader in national civic projects, and her brother a famous baseball player.

Pegeen was horrified at Mr. Massingill's brazen lying about her background. But she went through with the question-and-answer period following the show. She managed to remain completely vague about all things.

Raymond Massingill cleared the building twenty minutes later and, together with his wife, drove the still wigged and made-up Pegeen O'Hara to her car, careful first that no other car was following them.

"Well, goodnight, Pegeen," Mr. Massingill said as she was

changing cars. "I think the heat is off now. Just keep wearing that wig and makeup and everything'll be fine."

Pegeen got in her car, watched the Massingills drive off, and sat back in profound relief. She lighted a cigarette and started laughing to herself. As frightening as the beginning of her radio career had been, things were working themselves out into an enjoyable comedy for Pegeen O'Hara. If only she could tell her friends back at the BOQ. She did want to share it with someone—anyone. But she realized she simply could not take that chance. Maybe she could tell her sister when she went home for a weekend or on leave to Boston. Her sister could keep a secret.

Pegeen started her car and eased it out of the parking lot behind the local First National store. She drove up the town's main street and turned down the side street leading to the highway that linked the town and the base. She was waiting for the light to change when another car pulled up alongside her. The man looked over at Pegeen, winked, tipped an imaginary glass to his lips, and gave her a questioning look.

"Creep," Pegeen muttered under her breath. The light changed and she floored the accelerator, leaving the hopeful male at the intersection.

"Damn stuck-up bitch," Major Rip Ripples cursed as he drove away from the light toward his home. "They're all alike."

Rip Ripples watched the late news in his den that night. And there before him was a film clip of Doris O'Sheen during the interview at the radio station. He squinted to see better, careful not to arouse his wife, Sophia, who dozed in the chair next to him. It was the same girl he'd tried to pick up at the stoplight.

"I had her right there," Rip sputtered.

"What?" Sophia grumbled.

"Nothing."

"Well, if you've got nothing to say, don't say it. I'm trying to sleep."

"Yes, love." Ground glass in her oatmeal.

The next morning Rip Ripples stood before General Joplin in the general's office. Also present was Walter Buckles.

"She's got to be stopped," Buckles was saying as the general flew an F-111 model through the air with his hands. He made little jet noises every time he swooped low over the desk with the plane. "It's bad enough she's on public airwaves," Buckles continued, "but when the papers and television glorify and publicize her, that's too much for even a reasonable thinker like myself to bear."

"Schwooooooooo," the general went as he skip-bombed the file folders piled on the desk's edge.

"Well????" Buckles finally asked.

General Joplin landed the F-111 and swiveled around a couple of times in his chair. Major Ripples sat silently thinking of his intersection encounter with Doris O'Sheen. He'd decided not to mention the incident to anyone. It might get back to Sophia. He was thinking of how it would have been if she'd accepted his pantomime invitation for a drink last night. A couple of drinks, a local motel, and just as they'd undressed and were about to make love in the bed, he'd slip the handcuffs on her and ... No, he'd do that *after* they'd made love.

"Well????" The general was doing the asking this time. His question was directed at the daydreaming Rip Ripples.

"Give me a few days, General, and I'll have this O'Sheen thing settled. I've got a lead."

General Joplin turned to Walter Buckles. "See, Mr. Buckles. We're always on top of this Commie thing. Major Ripples here is an old pro in these matters. One of the top intelligence officers in the Air Force. Rest assured we'll have a complete rundown on Miss Doris O'Sheen within a week. Rest assured."

"Good." Buckles got up from his chair, saluted the general, realized he wasn't supposed to do that, and left the office.

"Don't let me down, Rip," the general said with great sincerity. "You've got to come through."

"Positive, sir."

The F-111 took off again as Major Rip Ripples went back to his office down the hall. There was a message on his desk to call Sophia.

"Hello, Sophia. This is Rip."

"Don't forget to be home early. This is my bowling night."

"Right, love. Oh, I just thought of something. I'm going to have to go out tonight, too. You'd better get a sitter."

"Where are you going?"

"Top secret, love."

Rip leafed through the copy of *Popular Science* until he came to the section on how brakes on a car work. He studied the diagrams as Sophia delivered a nonstop protest to his plans to leave the house that night. She eventually hung up just as Rip was beginning to understand the basic principle

238

behind why brakes work and, conversely, why they wouldn't work.

"No," he sighed. "She might run into someone else and kill them."

He left the house before his wife that night. They'd battled about his going, the resolution being his promise to pay the sitter out of his lunch allowance.

Rip went back to the intersection where he'd seen Doris O'Sheen the night before. He arrived there at seven and waited in his car a discreet distance back from where she might turn off the highway and enter town. It was a long shot but, in Rip's mind, a worthwhile one. He was deep in thought about asking Sophia for a higher lunch allowance when she appeared—the blue Ford, the long black hair, the rather prominent nose. He fell in behind her on the street and followed until she parked at the First National parking lot and entered Mrs. Massingill's car. Once they'd disappeared, Rip pulled his own car into the lot and parked it beside the blue Ford. He got out, looked around, and entered Pegeen's car. The glove compartment showed nothing of interest: Kleenex, local street map, mirror, comb, flashlight, and the welcoming booklet and map of the Air Force base.

Rip sat back in stunned silence. He fingered the welcoming book as if it were a highly valuable piece of fur. "Good God," he gasped, "she's infiltrated the base."

It had been Rip's plan merely to search the car and then, if possible, follow it when it was driven home by Doris O'Sheen. But the welcoming booklet and map placed a different emphasis on the whole plot. He'd have to act fast.

It didn't take long for a man of Ripples' intellect to decide what his next step must be. He walked to a phone booth and called General Joplin.

"General? Rip Ripples here. I can't talk long, but you were right. Miss O'Sheen is definitely subverted."

"You mean subversive, Ripples?"

"Yes. That's what I mean."

"How bad?"

"Bad."

"Base security involved?"

"Positive."

"Alert?"

"Not yet, General. Let me have a go at this first. My life instead of thousands."

"Yeah. Well, have at it, Rip. I'd like a report in the morning. Early."

"Roger. By the way, sir, have you ever met Sophia?"

"Loren?"

"Ripples. The little woman."

"No."

"I've got kids, General."

"Roger, Major. We won't forget."

"Over and out."

Rip Ripples went back to the parking lot and moved his car to a space on the street. He took a small crowbar from his trunk and carried it back to Pegeen's blue Ford. Again, looking carefully around to be sure he was alone, he set about prying open the trunk of her car. It sprang open, and he climbed into the trunk, cursing the loose jack that tore his new lounging slacks. He pulled the trunk hood down over him and waited in the cramped darkness. Only once did he falter when his jockey shorts cut deeply into his crotch.

"Damn it, Sophia, I told you to buy me summer shorts all year round."

The major was going over the Geneva Convention rules in his head when Mrs. Massingill drove up with Pegeen. Rip froze in his twisted position and listened. The door slammed.

" 'Night, Pegeen. Pretty soon all this will die down and everything will be normal."

" 'Night, Mrs. Massingill. And thanks for everything."

" 'Night, dear. Don't forget dinner Saturday night."

"I won't. I'm looking forward to it. And thanks."

Pegeen got in her car, started it, and pulled out of the lot. She eventually stopped at the same light where Rip had tried to pick her up, proceeded on the green, and turned onto the highway heading back to the base. She'd promised to meet Jackie and me at the Officers' Club at ten for a drink. Of course, we had no idea why she couldn't make it earlier. She just told us she'd be busy until about nine-thirty.

Rip crouched in the trunk counting off seconds.

". . . 809, 810, 811, 812 . . ." He'd seen a movie once where the hero knew how far they'd traveled by counting. "... 813, 814, 815 ..."

And then the siren. It started as a faint shrill far behind them and had developed into a powerful roar by the time Pegeen pulled off the highway and came to a bumpy halt on the grass. Rip was tempted to jump out and tell the policeman to be on his way; this was Rip's act and he didn't want anyone sharing the glory. But he thought better of the scheme.

Rip could hear the policeman get out of his car and approach Pegeen.

"License and registration, ma'am," he told her.

"What did I do, Officer?"

"Little over the limit, young lady."

"I didn't realize . . . I just thought . . ."

"It's OK. License and registration look in order. But take it easy from now on. OK?"

"Yes, sir, I certainly will."

Rip was sweating now. "Get the hell out of here," he mumbled under his breath. It seemed that was exactly what the policeman was about to do until his voice could be heard again.

"Just a second, ma'am. What's wrong with your tire?"

"My tire? I didn't know anything was wrong."

"Sure is something wrong. Looks pretty flat. Probably a slow leak. I'll change it for you and you get that fixed right away."

"Oh, please don't go to all that . . ."

"It's OK, ma'am. Happy to help. Let me have the trunk keys."

Major Ripples tensed into battle readiness as the police officer came around the back of the car and opened the trunk. At first he was surprised that it was already unlocked. But his initial surprise was nothing compared to his reaction when Rip Ripples leaped out of the trunk.

"Glad to see you, Officer. Major Ripples, United States Air Force Intelligence, on a special mission for General Joplin."

The policeman drew his gun.

Ripples jumped two feet into the air. "Put that down. Pleeeeeease."

"Hands on the car, mister," the policeman snapped.

"Now wait a minute . . . I told you I was . . ."

"I don't care if you're George Wallace. Hands on the car."

Major Ripples did as he was told. Inside the car, Pegeen O'Hara sat with her eyes straight ahead, peeking only occasionally in the rear-view mirror. It was Major Ripples. He'd spent three days in the base hospital with what they thought was a heart attack. It turned out to be only a reaction against his wife, Sophia. Pegeen could hear Major Ripples and the officer arguing as the policeman searched the major for weapons.

"The woman in this car is a Communist agent," Ripples muttered through clenched teeth. "The security of the nation is at stake."

241

"Ma'am," the policeman yelled, "would you come out here, please?"

Pegeen got out as directed and stood next to the infuriated Major Ripples.

"You know this man, miss?"

"Oh, my, no, sir. I . . . I never saw him before in my life."

"Are you a Communist agent, miss?"

"Oh, no, no, no, no, no. I'm . . . I'm . . . I'm Irish. From Boston."

"Do you have any idea why he was in your trunk, miss?"

Major Ripples straightened up and looked the officer straight in the eye.

"I was in her trunk because I was following her, you idiot. General Joplin will . . ."

"Get your hands on the car, mister." The policeman turned to Pegeen. "We'll go downtown, miss, and file charges against this guy. We see this all the time. These perverts follow girls home and then . . . well, rape usually follows."

"Don't call *me* a pervert, you—you—you pervert. I know what you were doing when you pretended to search me. Where's your discharge papers?"

Pegeen knew the ramifications of what would happen if she pressed charges. "Officer, I really don't want to press charges against this man. After all, he is a member of the Air Force and probably has a wife and children."

Ripples tried to pull a picture from his wallet, but the policeman hit his hand and the wallet fell to the ground.

"Please, Officer," Pegeen continued, "let him go. I think he's been scared enough never to try anything like this again."

The officer stood with a puzzled look on his face. "Gee, ma'am, I hate to let these kind of perverts go around loose. Think of the next girl."

"I know, Officer. I know. But please. Just this once. Maybe you've heard me on the air. My radio name is Doris O'Sheen."

"Doris O'Sheen? Sure I've heard of you. Say, your voice did sound familiar to me."

"That's not your real name?" Ripples asked excitedly. "What is your real name? Officer, I demand to know this Commie's real name."

"Why? So you can start making obscene phone calls or try to rape her again in her own home? Come on, buddy. I'll take you downtown and drop you off. Just thank your lucky stars this young lady is so lenient."

"Call General Joplin," Major Ripples protested as the policeman took him to his car. Pegeen got back in her car and drove off toward the base. By the time she arrived at the gate, the soft tire, forgotten in the contretemps with Major Ripples, was almost flat. She limped on to the base, parked at the BOQ and went to her room. She got rid of the makeup, stored the wig in its box, washed up, and walked over to the Officers' Club to meet Jackie and me.

We'd created a small party of our own at the club, and by eleven-thirty everyone was in the gayest of moods. Things would have progressed right into the early morning hours if the club hadn't been raided by the base military police, led by General Joplin and Major Rip Ripples.

It seems that after the policeman dropped Rip off at his car in town, Rip drove out to the base and went immediately to the general's home. He told the general that not only was Doris O'Sheen a Communist but that the entire police force in town was also under orders from Peking. The general, as involved as he was in the whole affair, really didn't put a lot of faith in his intelligence officer at that point. He dismissed Rip who, in a somber and sullen mood, drove around the base. Rip spotted Pegeen's car in the BOQ parking lot, verified his find by the flat tire, and went immediately to Personnel, where all vehicles were registered. They told Major Ripples who owned the blue Ford. He went back to the general.

"I know you were sleeping, General," Rip pleaded, "but this couldn't wait until morning. Doris O'Sheen is not Doris O'Sheen. She's Pegeen O'Hara, a nurse and an officer right here on this base."

They arrested Pegeen right there at the club and took her to Major Ripples' office for questioning. She admitted doing the radio show but denied being a Communist. A representative of the Judge Advocate's office was also present and advised General Joplin that it was imbecilic to try to prosecute Lieutenant O'Hara on the charge of Communism. But he did point out that she had broken regulations by taking a part-time job without permission.

Pegeen received a severe reprimand, quit her job as Doris O'Sheen, and continued to be a good Air Force nurse and officer. Walter Buckles did eventually start a talk show of his own in town and spent each evening accusing the Air Force of harboring known Communists. Major Ripples was assigned to Vietnam. Sophia left him to marry a local cop after some moonlighting of her own, which all goes to prove that wanting to be dead rather than Red doesn't make much sense at all.

Chapter 22

"*All Men Are Not Created Equal*"

As nurses, we see a lot of naked men. As a result of this exposure, we've come to a few conclusions:

1. All men are not created equal. No further comment seems necessary.

2. Beauty *is* only skin deep.

3. A man's physical attributes or inadequacies do not seem in any way to have resulted from or contributed to his choice of civilian occupation.

This third observation results from a game we sometimes play when confronted with officers with whom we're not acquainted. We've found it fun to try to guess the officer's civilian occupation. Airline stewardesses do the same thing, although they also try to establish a man's nationality. We don't carry the game that far. His profession is enough for us.

It would be misleading to have you think we make these judgments based only upon a man's body, the result of such surface guessing doomed to distinguish only whether the man was active or placid in his life.

No, we must also utilize the man's thoughts, his way of speaking, his mannerisms and habits.

Every military man has some civilian occupation, skill, or profession which he practiced before entering the Armed Forces. This is especially true of reserve officers and enlisted men who have been recalled to active duty in time of emergency and need. They've had time to develop their civilian jobs and, in turn, have more fully absorbed the effects of their jobs into their personal thinking.

Jackie and I have been surprisingly successful in this guessing game. Because of our proved success, we feel confident and not the least brash in presenting those general impressions upon which we depend when playing the game. Should you fall into any of the categories listed, we can only say that you shouldn't complain. Think of all the nasty things you've said about nurses in your life.

ADVERTISING MEN: Snap judgments are dangerous where ad men are concerned. Jackie fell victim once to snap-judging an officer to be an advertising man. She'd tried to bait him right off the bat and get him to talk.

"Say, Captain, what about the problem of Communist

infiltrators in the service? How do you think we ought to discover them and weed them out?"

"I know what I'd do," he answered. "I'd run the flag up the pole and see who saluted it."

"Advertising man," Jackie whispered to me.

She was wrong. He was a career officer from the age of seventeen. Jackie should have been more careful in her analysis. Obviously, the advertising and military professions have something in common.

Advertising men in the military are generally among the more easy-to-spot groups. Their way of dressing can be one tip-off. Former ad men will try to improvise on the basic and standard military uniform. They'll slip in their own style of black shoe, usually with tiny buckles or other "in" ornamentation. They'll tie their ties in bigger knots than regulation. They'll do anything to maintain contact with their former world, a world of conformity to just about everything. We suppose that's why all advertising looks alike.

Actually, advertising men make marvelous members of the Armed Forces. They're so used to conforming that they fall into military conformity rather nicely. Just imagine how secure they feel when they look around and realize they're wearing exactly what everyone else is wearing. There are no shocks to experience in the military such as they might have experienced on any given morning when catching the train to work. The ad exec exits his home wrapped securely in a five-button buckskin suit, suede shoes of the latest color green, wide polka-dot tie, and checkered shirt. He leaves the train in Manhattan and walks along the street. Just as he is about to enter his building, he sees the agency's leading fashion plate leaving the building. He has his five-button buckskin suit under his arm, walks to the sidewalk trash can, and deposits the suit therein. He goes back into the building.

The ad man fresh off the train stares at the suit in the trash can. And then the real horror hits him. The agency fashion plate was wearing a dark blue single-breasted suit with pleated pants and black shoes. It sends our hero racing to the nearest store on his lunch hour for a new wardrobe.

But in the service this same ad man can look around him at any time and breathe a deep sigh of contentment. Everybody looks alike. Everybody is "in."

You can also catch an ad man at a briefing on full-scale nuclear war. While the general is detailing the deaths-per-million in any given bombing situation, our ad man interjects cost-per-thousand figures.

Attend a budget meeting with an ad man, and while talk is of gaining additional funds from Congress, the ad man might suggest charging the federal government a fifteen percent commission on each bomb run.

Above all, former ad men tend to set a stage in everything they do. They dress for their role, adopt model's poses, decorate their offices and apartments in whatever stage setting is "in" at the moment, light their offices and homes in TV lighting tradition, and, in general, seem to live their lives by a script.

One girl we know started dating a bachelor officer, formerly an account executive for a large Madison Avenue agency. Four dates led them to the ultimate moment of truth in his BOQ room. He adjusted the lighting just so—a directional lamp the prime light source, a second lamp on the other side of the couch to add dimension, and a key light from above for hair highlights. The couple embraced on the couch. His hand slipped around from her back and clasped one of her breasts.

"Ooh, that's nice," she moaned and clutched him closer.

Suddenly he broke the embrace, got up, and went around and sat down on the other side of the girl.

"What's the matter?" she asked.

"Nothing. It's just nicer this way."

They resumed their embracing, but the girl noticed that the light was now striking her date in a more flattering way. He kissed her hard, pulled his lips away and looked deep into her eyes.

"This could be the beginning of a long career together," he said in his best throaty voice. Then he reached over to the end table and turned a knob. Music—dramatic string music—gushed forth from the speakers on the walls.

". . . a career that was destined to be . . ."

The girl gently pushed the ad man away and looked deep into *his* eyes.

"You know what, Mervin?"

"What?"

"Well . . . I don't know how to say this . . . Well, you've got *bad breath*."

"Bad breath?"

"I know. Even your best friend won't tell you."

"But I . . ."

"Don't worry. I'll bring you something. You can count on me."

Our girl friend got up and left.

"Did you tell him why you were leaving?" I asked her after she'd told us the story.

"Sure. I told him he'd paid for a one-minute spot and the minute was up. Maybe we'd do a special sometime. He seemed to understand."

"Did you ever see him again?" we asked.

"Sure. Once he started grabbing me all over. I told him to quit it. You know what he said? He said, 'You're in good hands with me.' Another time we were discussing the theory that Jewish girls were looser in their morals than other girls."

"He didn't?"

"Sure he did. He told me, 'You don't have to be Jewish to enjoy sex.' "

In retrospect, ad men are too easy to spot. We've modified our rules in regard to them. Now, in order to gain points, you also have to guess what account they worked on with their agency. It's only fair.

AUTOMOBILE MECHANICS: If a man has worked as a mechanic for more than a year, he becomes a total victim of his experience.

An airman comes in to sick call.

"What seems to be the trouble, Airman?"

"It's my neck. I have terrible pains in my neck."

"I see. Let me take a look."

The doctor tries to get his finger down the man's collar. He can't.

"No wonder you have pains in the neck, Airman. Your collar is too tight. Just open it up and you'll feel fine."

"Well, sir, it's not that simple. There's got to be something major wrong inside the neck."

"No, Airman. It's just as simple as I said."

"Look, sir, I don't want to argue with you, but I know my business . . . I mean my neck. It's going to take some major fixing to straighten my neck out."

"Such as, Airman?"

"Can't really tell without going in and looking. Might be a faulty valve. Or a clogged artery. Could even be linked in some way to bad heart muscle. In that case, I guess you'd have to replace the whole heart, huh, Doc?"

"Well, Airman, I just don't have the time to do all that. I'll just have to recommend you run around awhile the way you are and see what happens."

The airman is dejected.

"OK, Doctor. But if it causes a complete breakdown, don't

blame me. If it were your neck, I'd do a major overhaul right now!"

LIFE INSURANCE SALESMEN: It takes great skill and experience to spot a life insurance salesman early in the game. The difficulty arises because this breed of man lives two separate and distinct lives and personalities.

Socially, the former life insurance salesman is a bundle of laughs, an outgoing and fun-loving animal. You meet him at a party and the last thing you think of is that he could be in so grim a business as insuring people's lives.

Professionally, of course, the life insurance salesman is a merchant of gloom and despair. Jackie and I knew one who became friendly with us at a reception at the Officers' Club. He was a laugh-a-minute.

But he called us the following Monday morning.

"Hi. Harry Dirgeheim here."

"Oh, hi, Harry. How are you?"

"Fine. Fine. In the pink. I guess you never know, though. Oh, well. Frankly, I'm a little upset this morning."

"I'm sorry to hear that, Harry."

"Yes. Well, don't you worry yourself about it. Although maybe it does affect you. You remember Major Wolps, don't you?"

I searched my memory. Nothing.

"Never heard of him."

"Really? I was sure you knew him. Really tragic."

"What's tragic?"

"The way he went. Head-on. Yesterday."

"Oh, that's terrible."

"You don't know the half of it. I was an insurance consultant in civilian life. Still sell life protection on the side. Don't make any money out of it but want to be of service to my fellow man. I talked to Major Wolps just before he took that little weekend drive. He wanted to buy a policy from me but said he'd wait until Monday. Well, there'll be no more Mondays for Major Wolps. I feel so helpless."

I offered my sympathy to Harry Dirgeheim and hung up. What a shame, I thought.

Harry called the next Monday morning.

"Hi. Harry Dirgeheim here. How are you?"

"Great, Harry."

"Yeah. Say, you remember Bob Marks, don't you?"

"I don't think so, Harry."

"Yeah. Boy, it's upsetting. He had to wait over the weekend

before signing for that Golden Protection Exclusive Long-Life Convertible Rider Policy I had mapped out for him. I even managed to get rid of the war exclusion for good old Bob."

"Gee, that sounds grand."

"Yeah. Heart attack. Six kids. Hell of a mortgage, too."

"Wow."

"Yeah. Well, see you soon."

It went on like this for three more Mondays. Finally Harry made the pitch.

"Look, girls," he told us over drinks at the club, "what happens if either of you should die?"

"We don't think about that," we answered.

He shook his head back and forth slowly. "Yeah. You should think about it, believe me. Is it fair for your poor mothers and fathers to have to pay those burial expenses out of their own pockets?"

We eventually stopped seeing Harry Dirgeheim, even for occasional drinks at the club. He was simply too depressing once he took professional aim at us. Later a friend advised us how to discourage people like Harry Dirgeheim from pursuing us. When the insurance salesman says, "I'd like to talk to you about life insurance," you answer, "I'd love to talk about it. Now that I have this terminal heart condition, I could sure use some life insurance."

They always go away.

GAMBLERS: Most people don't realize that there are many civilians who make their living as gamblers. We're not talking about the once-a-week poker games at the neighbor's house. We're talking about the man who does nothing but play cards, roll dice, bet on horses, and fight the system in Las Vegas.

To many of these gamblers, the call to duty with Uncle Sam comes as a profound shock. But once they've been in the service for awhile, they realize it constitutes a gold mine for their particular talents. They look around and see a bunch of scared, skinny kids with nothing to do and a need to become manly overnight. Gambling, the smoke-filled room, men swearing and risking their stakes on the whim of the dealer or the throw of the dice, all seem to contribute to this needed manly image.

We've run into a number of gamblers at various bases. We remember one in particular who, after filling out five one-page forms, swirled the pages into a fan with a flick of his wrist, held them out to us, and said, "Pick one. Any one."

Occasionally a gambler will be caught and taken to task by his superiors. We've even known some who were courtmartialed for their gambling activity. But generally, these have been men who cheated and bilked a lot of money from enlisted men.

Ginger Whip went steady once with a gambler. At least that's what she told the handsome young lieutenant she met at the club one night. She'd asked what he did for a living, and he told her he was a gambler. They started going together, and he invited Ginger to come with him when he sat in at big-stakes games downtown. The game was run by three semipro gamblers in the town and they'd always done extremely well in games with Air Force personnel. Naturally, they were eager when Lieutenant Sharp sought them out and asked to be included in the games.

The lieutenant lived up to his name. He played it slow and cool the first few weeks, losing a little more than he won but always holding out the promise to the civilians that he was ready to lose everything.

At first the gamblers didn't like the thought of Ginger's attending the sessions.

"No broads," they told Sharp.

"Sorry," he answered, "but I want her here."

They relinquished. They didn't want to lose this new loser.

The first night Ginger got bored and walked around the table. She looked at the cards in one man's hands and said, "Oh, my, how did y'all ever make all those picture cards come together?"

"OUT!" the man screamed.

Lieutenant Sharp took Ginger aside and told her the facts of card games. "Don't open your mouth again," he said.

"I wouldn't think of it," she replied in a hurt but defiant tone.

Lieutenant Sharp gave Ginger a drink and went back to the game. She kept drinking as the game went on late into the evening, passed midnight, and headed for the early-morning hours. By that time Ginger was a babbling drunk.

"How about switching the game?" Lieutenant Sharp suggested before one deal.

"To what?" one of the players asked.

"Red Dog."

There was silence. The men looked at each other. Red Dog, that most vicious of card games, had been suggested. Its very mention brought shudders to the men around the table. Red Dog. The game played on all the ships coming back from World War II. Red Dog. The game in which men lost every cent of their hard-earned battle pay, sometimes thousands of dollars, in an hour. Red Dog.

"You sure you wanna play Red Dog?" one of the gamblers asked Lieutenant Sharp.

"Why not?" he answered.

Another gambler smiled.

"All right," he said. "The lieutenant wants to play Red Dog. Red Dog it'll be."

Lieutenant Sharp shuffled and dealt four cards to everyone. They picked their cards off the table one at a time, slowly, carefully, peeking as they placed each card into their hand. Ginger could sense that tension was building. She sat on the edge of her chair and watched through bleary eyes as each player carefully considered his chances of beating the card Lieutenant Sharp would overturn from the deck. It was that simple; bet what you would against the pot and hope you beat the next card up in suit. Each man had anted up one hundred dollars, but Sharp suggested they make it three hundred. There it was, eighteen hundred dollars in the middle of the table.

"Oh, my," Ginger sighed.

Sharp looked at the player on his left.

"How much?" he asked coldly.

"A grand."

Sharp flipped over the next card. Ten of hearts. The man to his left laid his four cards on the table. He had Jacks or better in every suit except hearts. His best in that suit was a nine. He tossed his thousand into the pot, got up, and left the room without saying a word.

"Next," Sharp said.

"I'm out."

"Next."

"Two thousand," was the reply. The man put the two thousand into the pot—forty-eight hundred now on the table.

Sharp turned over the card. Ace of spades. The bettor, now a loser, seemed ready to attack Sharp. But he restrained himself, got his coat, and left the room.

It finally got around to the last man at the table, the man immediately to Sharp's right. He thought for a moment, shook his head no, excused himself, and left Lieutenant Sharp and Ginger alone in the motel room.

"Whoopee," Ginger went as she fell off the chair.

Sharp ignored her. He quietly took the money from the table and counted it. Seventy-two hundred dollars. He smiled and turned to Ginger.

"How about a game, sweetie?"

"Oh, my, no," she said. "I'm just a li'l ol' workin' nurse. I don't have any money."

"You don't need money, sweets," he told her. "I just feel like playing some more. Come on. My money against your clothes."

Ginger giggled.

"Strip poker?" she asked with great disbelief.

"Yeah. You ever play?"

"Oh, my, no."

"Well, come on and try. You don't even have to worry about my motives. I'm not taking my clothes off. You can win money and I can win a look at that beautiful body of yours."

"I guess that's true," Ginger said. "My goodness, there's absolutely nothin' wrong with displayin' the human figure, now is there?"

"Nothing wrong at all, Ginger."

She sat at the table and Sharp dealt the cards. They'd play simple five-card poker, with each item of Ginger's clothing equal to a hundred dollars of Sharp's money.

Three hours later Ginger sat dressed only in her panties. In front of her was twelve hundred dollars. They'd played evenly all the way.

"Oh, my, looks like I'm down to my last asset," Ginger giggled.

"Sure does." Sharp was bleary-eyed by this time. He'd never expected Ginger to do so well in the game. He dealt another hand and lost another hundred. She dealt and again won. Sharp's eyes were riveted on the magnificent sight Ginger's bare breasts presented across the table. He couldn't even see her pants, but he knew he had to win them, had to have that final hand.

"I think we oughta stop and let me count my money now," Ginger said an hour later. She counted. "Oh, my, three thousand and seven hundred dollars. Oh, my."

Sharp had taken to the bottle during the past hour and was quite drunk.

"Ginger," he slurred, "how about taking off the pants for fun. OK?"

"Now just a minute, Mr. Lieutenant Sharp. Just what kind

a girl you think I am? If you want my pants, you just better start playin' a little better and win 'em."

Sharp reached across the table and grabbed one of her breasts.

"Now you stop that, heah? That certainly isn't polite for an officer and a gentleman."

"Please, Ginger. Just let me win this one. OK?"

"Now that just wouldn't be fair, now would it? Lettin' you win an' all."

"I can't stand to lose another hand," Sharp blubbered. "Here. Here's five hundred. Please. Take off your pants."

"Why, that would be like prostitution."

"Look, Ginger." Sharp was desperate now. "I'll deal one more hand, only I'll make sure I have the better cards. I'll win, you take off your pants, and then we'll play one more hand. You'll win that for five hundred. Jeez, Ginger, I've got to win one more hand. I'll never be able to play again unless I do."

As we've described previously, Ginger Whip is all heart. She realized how important winning was to Lieutenant Sharp.

"Oh, my, my honey." She stood up, slipped out of her pants and sat on his lap. "You poor deah."

Sharp had one moment of carnal instinct. But he just grinned, kissed Ginger on the cheek, and fell asleep right there in the chair. She cradled his head to her bosom and hummed, "Lullaby . . . and goodnight . . ."

Gamblers make bad officers . . . and husbands.

MOVIE PEOPLE: We're not referring to movie stars. They seldom serve in the Armed Forces, and for good reason. The young ones have large responsibility supporting their parents . . . and servants . . . in the mansion. The older stars generally marry just as another world crisis is breaking out, this accounting for their constant civilian status and frequent marriages.

No, the movie people to whom we refer are those cameramen, grips, assistant directors (full directors manage to avoid Uncle Sam, too), lighting technicians, sound men, and general flunkies.

Men in the movie business are very much behind the times. To begin with, they want you to know immediately that they're in the motion picture business.

"Good morning, Airman," you say as he enters the clinic for his physical.

"Hi-ho, Lieutenant." He makes a little rectangle of his fingers and views you through it.

We chuckle. "Say, what are you doing?"

"Framing you. I'm in the movie business."

We suppose they feel all girls will immediately strip and lie down for a shot at Hollywood. Nonsense. Those days went out with the Fifties. Girls just aren't star-struck anymore.

Movie people are very fun-loving. They're used to extended trips on location and are constantly looking for ways to break the monotony of small towns and bad food. A civilian girl friend of Jackie's went out on a blind date once with a motion picture cameraman. There were seven of them at the restaurant when the local police broke in and arrested everyone. It seems the cameraman slipped a note to the waiter, saying: "HELP! I'm being held captive by a band of deviates." The waiter took it seriously and called the police.

And so on.

Sometimes it's very confusing when a motion picture man conducts drill for new recruits.

"Quiet on the set," he screams when he wants them at attention.

"Action!" when it's time for them to march forward.

"Print that," he says when they look good.

"Mark it and strike it," he bellows when the drill has been completed.

Movie people generally end up as cooks and truck drivers in the service.

LAWYERS: Unfortunately, many of the problems in the service stem from the mismatching of men and jobs. We had a medical corpsman in Massachusetts who'd completed his law schooling but hadn't passed the bar exam before entering the Air Force. He was determined to become a great trial lawyer when his military obligation was over, and he could think of nothing else while working at the hospital.

It was his job to conduct preliminary questioning of patients when they came in for sick call. He'd ask the questions and make notes to give the doctor who would examine and treat the man.

One day a crusty sergeant came in with abdominal pains. He sat down and started to tell the corpsman what was ailing him.

"Before we go into that, Sergeant, you do promise to tell the truth, the whole truth, and nothing but the truth, don't you? So help you God?"

"What the hell are you ..."

"Never mind, Sergeant. First, what is your name?"

The sergeant started to give his name, but the corpsman interrupted.

"... and your occupation."

"Sergeant Walter Grimsley ... Wait a minute ... My occupation is the same as yours."

"That's injecting a personal opinion, Sergeant, and is irrelevant. Please answer the question."

This went on for ten minutes, the sergeant becoming more confused and irritated as the questioning continued. Finally he blew.

"What the hell is this—a general court-martial or a medical exam?" he snarled at the young corpsman.

"You're in contempt, Sergeant. Any further outburst will find you ..."

The doctor came in at this point and saved the airman from physical harm. The law student never really did adjust to his bad assignment and took to drinking. The last we heard he'd re-upped and was in Vietnam.

RETAIL STORE OWNERS AND SALESMEN: Men who have worked in this civilian area of industry are difficult and seldom to be trusted.

The basic problem comes from their ingrained outlook on people. It becomes especially acute when they enter into an affair with a young lady.

They are the most exemplary gentlemen during the courting period. They bend over backwards for the girl, woo her, say the nicest things, and guarantee their lifelong love and fidelity.

But that all comes to an end once they've successfully sold her and delivered the merchandise. God help her if she should become pregnant by the guy.

"Stanley, I'm pregnant. And you did it."

"So what do you want from me? A lifetime guarantee? Look, I'm busy with someone else. Send a letter."

Unfortunately, the Better Business Bureau doesn't help in such matters.

ATHLETES: You can always tell an ex-athlete by the way he tosses everything around. One will come in for a physical, pick up the stapler from the desk, and toss it up in the air and from hand to hand.

Leave him for a minute and he's practicing his golf swing.

Ask him to pick something up off the floor and he'll toss it to you through his legs, like a center in football.

Put him in front of a mirror and he shadow boxes.

And all athletes talk Southern and use bad English. Even those from the North with a Harvard or Yale education affect a Southern accent and a good-ol'-boy bad-grammar way of speaking. It all has to do with image, we guess. The sports fan doesn't trust an intelligent athlete. We should also mention that we agree with stewardesses who claim athletes are the cheapest dates. There's no doubt about it.

UNION WORKERS: Men who are employed by labor unions enter the service with a distinct disadvantage. Their civilian job conditions them to view any group of people over three as in need of organization. Picture the torment when a union man enters the Air Force, looks around, and realizes there are hundreds of thousands of people, all engaged in the same line of work and all without collective bargaining.

Actually, their thoughts would not be without justification. Nowhere could collective bargaining be put to better use than in the case of all the enlisted men of the Armed Forces. But, conversely, nowhere would it prove more unworkable.

There has been an attempt of late to unionize the military. All the reputable unions have turned their backs on such an idea. However, certain hippie organizations have been publishing literature and holding meetings and trying to sign up a membership. It's proved to be an unsuccessful effort.

But think of the ramifications of a unionized Armed Force. The enemy is approaching. The squadron commander knows he must launch a lightning offensive to save his unit. He calls his assistant over to him in the foxhole.

"Bill," the commander says with gravity, "we're in bad trouble. We have to attack immediately or be wiped out sitting here on our duffs. I want you to send Mazminski out with a small patrol."

"Gee, I'm all for that, Captain, But it's Mazminski's birthday."

"So what?"

"Well, if you'll remember back to our last bargaining session, we won that point about getting your birthday off."

"All right. Send Weber."

"Well, sir, I can't. It's his wife's birthday. We won that, too."

"Jesus, man, we're about to be slaughtered here. Who do you have to lead a patrol?"

The assistant looks at his watch.

"Frankly, sir, no one. Well, not for the next half-hour. We're in the afternoon break."

The captain sits in the foxhole and sulks. The assistant, sensing his commander's dejection, smiles and slaps him on the shoulder.

"Look, sir, I have an idea. Maybe I can talk to the men and get them to give up the break this afternoon. Of course, I'll have to promise them overtime tonight. But the wage budget for the unit looks good, and I think I can get them to come around."

Suddenly the enemy leaps up from the surrounding brush and charges the unit. The men are outnumbered by at least a hundred to one.

"Sir," the assistant says, "would you sign these workmen's comp forms before you get involved in anything else. Some of the boys are having lower-back problems and . . ."

LOCAL POLITICIANS: We make a distinction between politicians of a national reputation and those who hold office in smaller geographical areas. The major reason for this distinction is that we've never seen a national politician in the Air Force. That doesn't prove they aren't in the service; it just means *we* haven't seen them.

This distinction is academic only. All politicians are alike, without exception. Our first clue to having a former politician in for a physical is the way he answers even the simplest questions.

"Have you ever fainted or blacked out, sir?"

"Oh, no. Definitely not, although I'm all for that sort of thing provided proper checks and balances are utilized."

"Huh?"

"Where you from, young lady?"

"Kansas."

"I'm from Florida. You're out of my district."

"Yes, sir."

"Now, what else do you want to know about me?"

"Your weight, sir. Has it changed greatly in the past year?"

"Not really, although I tend to lean a little to the right when called upon for a decision."

"How's your heart?"

"It depends on the issues."

"Any history of measles?"

"Listen, you can go all the way back. I'm clean."

The other tip-off on a politician comes when he's assigned. He will always find himself assigned to the coziest and easiest job on any base. If asked how he managed this, he'd undoubtedly reply, "The wisdom of the people must never be doubted."

"Amen!"

REAL ESTATE SALESMEN: We spotted our first real estate salesman within minutes after he entered the hospital. We escorted him into the examination room. He looked around, frowned a little, and said, "What's this go for? About six bucks a square foot?"

Naturally, we couldn't answer his question. But he had many more.

"This copper?" he asked as he washed his hands.

"What's it cost to heat this place?"

"Any termites?" He asked this very hush-hush.

It's difficult to get a straight answer from a former real estate salesman. We had one like this, and he proved to be a master evader.

"Weight, sir?"

"Two-sixty."

"Height?"

"Five-ten. But don't look upon that as a disadvantage. It actually provides more rigidity than a lighter frame. Sort of custom-built."

"Any history of heavy breathing?"

"Sure. But that's a plus sign, especially in the winter. Let's the old stale air out and keeps the pipes from freezing."

The military has found one major advantage to recalling real estate salemen. They never become the slightest bit upset when asked to work on the weekends.

AIRLINE EXECUTIVES: Airline executives recalled into the Air Force tend to carry over their civilian job attitudes into their military life. This can be bothersome. They can't resist suggesting ideas to the command that were A1 with the commercial airlines but are of no value to the Air Force.

"Gentlemen," a former airline man will tell his fellow officers at a staff meeting, "I think I've got some solid ideas concerning air evacuation flights from the war zone."

Everyone nods and awaits these gems.

"Basically, the load factors on these flights have been slipping lower and lower. More space aboard the aircraft with less use of that space. We've got to fill those litters."

It's pointed out that this would mean creating more casualties in the war.

"No matter," the airline exec answers. "Besides, we've got to consider aircraft utilization when peace comes. The men have to be enticed on our planes."

The leader of the staff meeting tries to go on to another topic, but our airline man isn't to be stopped.

"You all know I've been advocating the use of stewardesses on all military flights. Well, it's obvious you won't buy that plan, regardless of the fact that the use of pretty girls has proved extremely successful on commercial airlines. So I'm about to offer another idea that not only will provide a level of service aboard all flights but will also solve the pressing problem of what to do with our out-of-work Asian allies. I'd like to see Asian houseboys on each flight. With the right music, good food, chopsticks . . . the works . . . we can not only make flying a joy again but can further cement the excellent relations we enjoy with our Asian neighbors."

The other officers allow him to say his piece, and then they slide on to other matters. But at the very end of the meeting he has one final say.

"One final thing, gentlemen. Air Force planes are drab. I'd like to see them pastel, with pilots wearing uniforms to match."

Up Up and Away!

Chapter **23**

"*The Only Girl in Town*"

Carolyn Polaski arrived at the radar station on the first of October. She flew in on the C-47, was taken to her quarters, showered, unpacked, and set out for a leisurely walking tour of her new home. It was hot, but she expected that. The installation was small, but that, too, was to be expected. Advance radar posts were never very large. That was all right with Carolyn. She was from a very small town in the Midwest, and big cities always frightened her.

Carolyn thought it quaint that her room would be right there in the medical building. It was a tiny four-room building, air-conditioned and clean. She hadn't bothered seeking out the other nurses and their rooms. She'd have time for that later.

Carolyn eventually walked back to her room and lay down. She dozed off but was awakened by the ringing of the phone in the hall. She answered it and was greeted by a man's voice.

"Lieutenant Polaski?"

"Yes."

"This is Colonel Matt Marshall. Base commander."

Carolyn was flustered.

"Yes, sir. How are you, sir?"

"Just fine, just fine. I'm calling to invite you to dinner with me tonight. Sort of official welcome. Will you come?"

Carolyn was taken aback at the colonel's tone. She wasn't used to being given a choice by superior officers.

"Of course I'll come, sir."

"Good. The mess hall at six?"

"I'll be there."

Carolyn spent a long time primping before her dinner engagement. She was a pretty girl with a trim figure and pleasant personality. Satisfied that she looked her best, she went to the one mess hall serving the entire outpost. Officers and enlisted men mingled together freely. There was a screen partitioning off a small section of the large room, presumably for the officer corps. But it was empty except for one man, a colonel, who sat alone at a table. On the table were flowers and a tablecloth. And Carolyn was surprised to see water glasses of red wine at each of the three place settings.

The colonel spotted Carolyn and immediately got up and came to her.

"Lieutenant Polaski, I'm Colonel Marshall. Welcome."

He led her to the table, pulled out her chair, and joined her.

"We'll have one other guest for this dinner, Lieutenant,"

264

he said. "Captain Wheeliss will be dining with us. He's our base chaplain."

Captain Wheeliss soon joined them at the table. He was a large, pleasant man and obviously got along nicely with Colonel Marshall.

"One word of caution, Lieutenant," the chaplain said as he gulped down his wine. "Alcoholic beverages of any kind are prohibited here under our treaty with the local Arabs. We smuggle this in for religious services, but if they ever found out, we'd be in trouble. Drink up and we'll wash the glasses."

Carolyn did as he suggested. Dinner was served, and the three of them soon became very relaxed. There was a lot of laughter, and Carolyn noticed a number of the men in the open area of the room looking over and whispering. The chaplain sensed it, too, and suggested that they leave the dinner table and retire to his office.

When they were seated comfortably in easy chairs in his office, the chaplain poured another offering of wine.

"Carolyn," he said, "you are in a most unusual position at this base. Up until now we've never had a nurse on duty. The doctoring was handled by a med-tech. But Colonel Marshall has always felt we needed a more qualified person to administer to the needs of our men, and our request for a nurse was granted. That's why you're here."

Carolyn started to tell them how pleased she was to be of help, but Captain Wheeliss went on.

"Unfortunately, you're the only nurse here. In fact, you're the only female member of the team."

"I sort of gathered that," Carolyn said, sipping her wine. "I guess it should be sort of every girl's dream."

"Yes, I suppose it would be. But it can be difficult, too. I'm sure you can understand that."

"Oh, yes. I can imagine the problems."

Colonel Marshall picked up the conversation. "I've placed great faith in Captain Wheeliss. When men are this isolated, they need some strong spiritual guidance. That's why the chaplain is my most valued staff member. And I believe he'll be of great help to you. Hopefully, he'll be able to prevent problems before they become problems."

The three of them spent another two hours discussing Carolyn's assignment. It was the chaplain's feeling that she could prove of great value in giving the men a positive and pleasant experience. It would be good to have a pretty, pleasant girl to talk with, eat with, and enjoy.

"But it would also be easy for you to slip into an unhealthy

265

pattern of sex, Carolyn. These men have been without a woman for a long time. Only your conscience can guide you in this matter, but if you start something, it could get completely out of hand."

Carolyn spent the next two weeks getting acclimated and settled. She was kept busy administering to minor ills and arranging for more seriously sick patients to be evacuated back to the States. She enjoyed her job and enjoyed the looks of adoration from the men. Of course, there were also looks of lust, some coming from attractive men that inspired a few lustful thoughts of her own. But she tried, successfully, to ignore these, and went about her business of being a nurse.

Soon she began to receive offers to join certain men for dinner. And lunch. And breakfast. Coffee breaks. Milk shakes. Card games. Watching old movies. Horseshoes. Darts. Scrabble. Monopoly. Dice. Anything. The colonel and the chaplain weren't against this, so Carolyn began accepting some of the offers. She soon found herself accepting more and more offers, to such an extent that she was having difficulty keeping track of them. She missed a few because of schedule conflicts, which caused a great deal of hard feelings among the men. One of them even went to the chaplain and complained.

"Sir, all I wanted to do was play cribbage with her. I've been upset for a week over it. I asked for another date, and she said she was busy for the next three weeks. What's wrong with me? I mean, do I have bad breath or something?"

The chaplain called Carolyn into his office, and they discussed the problem.

". . . and so, Carolyn, I'm about to do something unheard of in military history. I'm about to assign my own chaplain's assistant to you as a social secretary. He'll book your appointments and handle your schedule. All requests will come through him for your consideration. All I ask of you is to please try to accommodate everyone at least once. It means so much to them. And by the way, you haven't fallen victim to any carnal thoughts, have you?"

Carolyn admitted she'd had a few but had been strong.

"Good girl. Keep it up."

The chaplain's assistant, a nice young man, sat down with Carolyn and they plotted out a schedule and a system to keep it in order. While they were talking, Carolyn received a phone call.

"Ma'am, this is Sergeant Boomer McGregor. I'd like the

pleasure of your company at the movie on December eleventh of this year."

Carolyn looked at her social secretary.

"Sergeant, I'd love that. But I must ask you to contact Airman Pious, my aid. He'll check my schedule and advise you of my availability."

Pious beamed.

"I won't let you down, ma'am."

"I know you won't, John. And thank you. This takes a great load off my shoulders."

Airman John Pious did his job well. Of course, he did alienate a few of the men with his brisk and efficient handling of their requests. But by and by, everyone came to accept the system as practical and necessary. There were, of course, a few jokers who would call Airman Pious.

"Would you check your schedule and see if Lieutenant Polaski is booked on the night of August twenty-first? I'd like two hours of sack time with her."

Pious ignored such phone calls.

One evening, after nine months had flown by, Airman Pious sat down and held a briefing for Carolyn, the chaplain, and Colonel Marshall.

"I've made a chart," he told them, "that indicates the success of Mission Carolyn. That's the name I've given this project, sirs. I hope you don't mind."

They smiled their approval.

"To date, and that includes this morning, Lieutenant Polaski has been entertained by every man on the base an average of 6.7 times. Now that doesn't include you two gentlemen. Or me, I'm afraid. This study is broken down into man-minutes, and I've assigned an effectiveness scale to the different types of entertaining. Dinner, of course, counts highest on the scale of effectiveness. Coffee dates are, in my estimation, more effective than movies or games because there is a more direct flow of communication.

"I also have kept records of problems directly alleviated by Lieutenant Polaski. She's talked three men out of suicide, settled eleven difficulties with wives back home, helped soothe thirty-seven sets of broken hearts over girl friends back home, and convinced one man to re-up when his enlistment is up."

The report was well received. Pious walked Polaski back to her room and stood outside her door saying goodnight. Then, to his great surprise, she reached out, cupped his face in her hands, and kissed him on the lips.

"I'm sorry I've neglected you, John. Please accept as my apology the one and only kiss I'll give all year."

"You mean you haven't even kissed any of the other guys?"

"Not a one. Not that I didn't want to. I am a girl, you know. But I've been afraid to start something that would get out of hand."

Airman Pious didn't wash his face for two days. A few of his friends remarked that he looked pretty cocky, with his smug smile and springy step, but he just dismissed it on the grounds that he was getting close to rotation back home.

Eventually it did come time for Carolyn to rotate back home herself. The entire base turned out in dress uniform. There were many speeches, four men who played musical instruments gave out with some songs, and a few men even wept. Carolyn thanked everyone for their goodness and was throwing kisses when the aircraft appeared on the horizon, swept in low, and landed on the temporary strip. The door opened and out stepped Carolyn's replacement. She was old, mean, and tough-looking. She strode right over to the colonel, threw a sharp salute, and introduced herself.

"Colonel, I'm Major Birdwell reporting for duty."

The colonel greeted her and took her over to Carolyn. He introduced them, then brought in Airman John Pious.

"Airman Pious here has been assigned as a sort of special assistant to Lieutenant Polaski," the colonel said. He smiled and continued. "Being the only female here could have posed some pretty serious problems, but we managed to work out a . . ."

"Don't worry about me, sir," the new nurse said in a gravel voice. "The last man who tried to get fresh with me is doing a year in the stockade."

Carolyn fought to hold back the tears as she bade farewell to everyone and climbed aboard the plane for her trip back home. She looked down as they became airborne and said a little prayer for the new and only girl on the base.

Chapter 24

"Here Come de Truck . . . Here Come de Truck!"

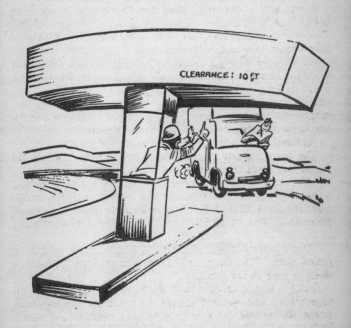

CLEARANCE: 10 FT

It's really been a temptation in writing this book to dwell on the problems between military installations and nearby civilian towns. The temptation stems from the simple fact that these two factions seem to be always at war with each other. There doesn't seem to be a day in which some squabble doesn't arise involving soldiers and civilians. An airman rapes a local girl. A GI goes to bed with a local girl and she *calls* it rape. A member of a military installation gets drunk and wrecks a local bar. A local girl rapes a GI. A Navy man sells pornographic pictures in town after bringing them back from Saigon. A soldier steals a car. The police chief's wife rapes a GI. And always, as with rape, military men buy too much at local stores and forget to pay the debt. Company adjutants spend their lives counseling their men on how to satisfy these bad debts. These adjutants even write letters for the debtors to the creditors, pleading understanding.

Mr. Paul Pinchfist
Manager
Easy Come-Easy Go Department Store.
U.S.A.

Dear Mr. Pinchfist:

I'm writing in reference to the debt of Airman Joseph Zwilp to your store.

Obviously, Airman Zwilp should not have purchased the color TV, water skis, eight suits, wristwatch, cuff links, seventy-five long-playing record albums, shotgun, tape recorder, twelve peek-a-boo pantie and bra sets, and electric guitar—with amplifier. As you probably know, Airman Zwilp's basic pay is eighty dollars a month.

We've managed to make arrangements with the imported car agency on his purchase of the Triumph. We'd like to make a similiar arrangement with you.

Will you accept one dollar a week from Airman Zwilp? We make this offer in good faith.

Thank you.

Yours truly,
Lieutenant Jasper Smoother
Adjutant

This was a smart adjutant. He never brought up the question of why Mr. Pinchfist extended credit in the first place to someone making eighty dollars a month. That would not have been prudent and probably would have set off a whole chain of negative reactions from the town's Chamber of Commerce.

It was also wise that the adjutant didn't ask about the store's credit structure. The Mafia could take a lesson from many stores who sell to military personnel.

But, be that as it may, settling debts takes up the greater part of any adjutant's time.

As a result of all the antagonism between local communities and military installations, the Armed Services constantly work toward better relations. And, in some instances, the civilian community reciprocates.

One graphic example of a civilian community making peace overtures came in Texas while we were on TDY for advanced training. There had been a whole series of incidents leading to deeply imbedded bad feelings between the factions. In this case, the townspeople felt they had contributed to the trouble and therefore decided to make amends.

"General," the representative of the Chamber of Commerce said, "we're going to build you a pretty new entrance on the north side of the base. A real showpiece. It will be our contribution to this base and acknowledge its importance to our town."

The general was pleased. Arrangements were made for construction to begin, and soon the new north entrance to the base was beginning to take shape. It was modern, of sandstone, in the shape of a large T. Its base was a tall, thin, telephone booth-like structure to house the guard. Above it, jutting out like wings, were two slabs of the sandstone forming a roof over either roadway that passed from the highway into the base. Actually, there was a third roadway that ran beyond the edge of the left roof. This was planned to accommodate those vehicles too tall to fit under the roof.

Dedication Day approached, and much to-do was made of the event. The general arranged for two Congressmen from the state to fly in for the dedication. The base band was on hand to play appropriate inspirational numbers. The entire Chamber of Commerce turned out, as well as the mayor, members of the City Council, and two women from the local community theater group. Perhaps their presence was most indicative of all.

The new sandstone entrance was officially presented to the general by the mayor after an hour of speech-making. We all stood in formation and watched as the speeches ground on.

They were climaxed by the president of the local Little League linking the entrance and the goodwill gesture it represented to playing the game for fun as opposed to playing to win. The town's championship team of the previous year cheered as he concluded his talk.

The general cut the ribbon. The beauty queen of the town posed with him.

And then the most important phase of the ceremony took place. The general proudly handed the key to the guardhouse to the entrance's first guard, a tall, handsome Negro airman from the base Air Police unit. He proudly saluted, opened the guardhouse, and the base had a new functioning entrance.

The general hosted a luncheon at the Officers' Club following the ceremony, and the festive air and gay spirit indicated a truly renewed and reinforced spirit of cooperation between the base and the community.

As the celebrating officials ate dessert and sipped coffee, the guard at the new entrance prepared to greet the first vehicle to use the new facility. He saw it, a delivery truck from the local food wholesaler, turn off the highway and proceed up the roadway that would bring him to the right side of the guardhouse. It was a familiar truck to the airman; he'd seen it many times while on guard duty at the other entrance to the base. It came three days a week to deliver food to the various clubs on base and was always driven by a fat and jolly employee of the wholesaler.

The airman stepped just outside the guardhouse and waved the truck to the outside lane where it wouldn't have to pass under a roof. As it approached, he narrowed his eyes against the sun's glare. He wasn't sure. He cast a quick glance upward at the overhanging sandstone roof. He looked back at the truck.

"Uh ... oh," he mumbled, frantically waving the truck to the outside lane. He noticed out of the corner of his eye that his commanding officer was approaching. "Look out!" he yelled. "Here come de truck!"

It came. The driver thought the airman was waving him right through. He gave it a little extra gas and threw the airman a little salute just as the top of the truck caught the sandstone overhang. It crumbled with a resounding WHOOOMPPPLLL. As it moved, it also twisted the steel substructure of the guardhouse, and that disintegrated before everyone's eyes. The airman had fled to the safety of the surrounding bushes and was joined there by his commanding officer.

There isn't much more to tell in this tale except that the celebrants from the club came by the new entrance ten minutes later and a few of them cried. It would be far too philosophical to chalk the incident up to destiny; the two factions were never meant to work together. And it would be flippant to condemn all do-gooders as troublemakers. Suffice it to say that this incident is simply one we recall with a chuckle now and then. We thought we'd pass it along.

Chapter 25

"Jail Bait . . . or, No One Is All Bad"

Every military installation has its stockade. We all know what a stockade is. Inside, against their will, are the misfits, the rebels, the undesirables, the bad, and the ugly. Criminals. Captured AWOL cases. Homosexuals. Muggers. Rapists. Smart alecks who didn't salute. Bad guys.

I came to know our stockade intimately. My exposure to it was not by design. Rather, it was forced upon me as a matter of duty, and I could do no less than live up to that duty.

People confined to the stockade become ill, like anyone else. And rather than take the chance of removing the prisoner to the hospital, stockade officials prefer to bring medicine to the prisoner.

Naturally, when someone is really sick, a doctor is dispatched to the stockade and performs his magic right in the cell. Some stockades have medical treatment rooms, but not all. Ours did, and sick prisoners were treated in that room unless their problem was grave enough to require the use of the hospital.

The nurses rotated in accompanying doctors to the stockade, and occasionally a nurse was dispatched for some minor problem that the doctors didn't wish to bother with. That's when I had my glorious experience with Mal Justine, nicknamed "The Savage" by his fellow inmates. I'd gone to the stockade to give routine vaccinations and was protected in the medical treatment room by three young Air Police. I completed the shots and was preparing to leave when the desk sergeant came to me.

"Lieutenant, we've got a prisoner who's sick. Can you see him?"

"Of course. What's his problem?"

"Rape, ma'am."

"I don't mean that, Sergeant. What's his sickness?"

"He says his stomach hurts, ma'am. Real bad."

"Well, bring him right in."

"Yes, ma'am. Only I should warn you. He's called The Savage. A real bad actor."

"The Savage?"

"Yes, ma'am. Six feet three, two-fifty if he's a pound. Mean as a snake, too. I'll get a whole detail in here with him."

I started to protest the need for such protection, but the sergeant had already turned and gone to fetch the prisoner. I waited a few minutes before the door was flung open and The Savage stomped into the room. Based on physical evaluation, he was aptly named. His hair was wild and black, his

276

eyes burned with hatred, and his mouth was twisted into a permanent animal sneer. He looked at me and curled his lip like a jungle cat ready to pounce. I must have jumped a little, because his mouth twisted into a nasty grin.

"I hate officers," he snarled.

I nodded that I knew what he meant.

"Shut up, Savage," the sergeant snapped.

"I hate you, too," The Savage answered back.

"You want solitary again, Savage?"

"It ain't so bad. I don't have ta look at your ugly puss dere." His voice was low and raspy.

We all stood there glaring, and I realized I'd better take charge.

"OK, Airman Justine. Up on the table."

"I ain't gettin' up on no table."

"So die." I started packing up my things.

"Up on the table, Savage," the sergeant ordered.

"Up yours, bum."

Two of the Air Police lifted their sticks, but I raised my hand to stop them. I looked into The Savage's eyes and thought I saw, down deep and far behind the ruthless haze of black, a human being.

"Would you leave us alone?" I asked the sergeant.

"No, ma'am. Not on your life."

I looked again at The Savage. I was confident I could handle him.

"Sergeant, I'm afraid I'm going to have to order you and your men to leave the room. It's for the good of the patient."

The sergeant thought a moment and, surprisingly enough, left the room and took his Air Police with him. "But we'll be right outside, ma'am. We can be in here in a second if you need us."

"Good, Sergeant."

I must admit I suffered a momentary lapse of confidence. The moment the door slammed behind them, I was tempted to call out and bring the guards back. But I knew I had to be strong, both for my sake and for the sake of my fellow nurses, scorned and dismissed by the supposed superior male majority of the Armed Forces. I stiffened, forced a smile on my face, and looked The Savage straight in the eye.

"Lie down!"

His hand came out at me in a reflex action, like a big cat when treed.

"Down!"

He grunted. And he sat on the edge of the examining table.

"Lie down!"

The Savage's face was set in a look of profound puzzlement. He tried to say something but finally just did as he was told and stretched out on the table.

"Where does it hurt?" I asked.

A big grin broke out on his face, and he grasped his crotch.

"Pig," I muttered. I opened my little doctoring kit and took out a stethoscope. I also tried to make conversation.

"Where were you assigned before ending up in here, Airman Justine?"

"Finance," he mumbled. He reached suddenly and grabbed my thigh with his ham-hock hands.

I brought my fist down with middle knuckles extended and caught him right in the bicep. He grunted and relaxed his hold.

"Do that again, mister, and I'll use the scalpel."

The Savage understood.

"Now," I continued, "where does it hurt?"

He pointed to the left side of his stomach.

"Pull up your shirt."

An amazing thing happened. This madman, this rapist, this savage grabbed hold of his belt, took on a pleading expression, and shook his head back and forth.

"Come on," I said. "Pull up your shirt."

He wouldn't.

I reached down, grabbed his shirt, and yanked it up. He fought with me to keep his shirt down, but I won. I gave his surprisingly soft belly a shove. He broke out in hearty laughter.

"Don't do that," he moaned. "I'm ticklish."

I did it again. He roared. I started laughing, and soon The Savage and I were two helpless laughing fools. The door flew open and the sergeant burst into the room, followed by the Air Police. They all went for Airman Justine, but I stopped them by standing in their way.

"Get out!" I ordered. "Everything's fine."

They muttered their protests but backed out of the room. Once the door was closed again, I gave The Savage another poke in the stomach. He laughed again and made a tentative reach for me. I looked down at him and said, "Go ahead. I'm not ticklish." He tickled me and proved me a liar. The room

278

was again filled with laughter. I finally couldn't take it anymore and backed away from the table.

"Did you really rape somebody?" I asked, gasping for breath.

"Nah. She wanted it, but then she didn't like it so she yelled rape."

"She didn't like it?"

"Nah. I got a problem. Every time I do it I start laughing. Lieutenant, you got no idea how easy I tickle."

"Oh, I do, Savage. I do."

"Yeah. I guess you do at that."

I asked a few more questions, and it became evident that Airman Mal Justine's stomachache was the result of simple constipation. I prescribed a laxative, ordered a daily dose of prune juice, and left the stockade, much to the relief of the sergeant and his men.

"I don't mind telling you, Lieutenant, that you were in with a really bad actor. Worst type I've seen in here in ten years. You're real lucky, and I wouldn't advise anything so foolish again, if you don't mind my saying so."

"I don't mind, Sergeant. I'll try to be more careful in the future."

I didn't think much more about Airman Mal "The Savage" Justine until three weeks later when his court-martial came up. I remembered two court-martials I'd sat through as a spectator and how appalled I'd been at the casual lack of concern or attention exhibited by the members of the court-martial board. One actually fell asleep, another quietly read a magazine while the defense was presenting its case, and a third board member completed two full crossword puzzles during the proceedings.

And then I thought of Airman Justine, whose greatest crime, it seemed to be, was being too ticklish.

So I marched down to the Judge Advocate's office and asked to see the defense attorney assigned to Airman Justine's case. I was led into a cubicle and introduced to a young captain named Jud Mason.

"Captain Mason, I'd like to volunteer as a character witness on behalf of Airman Mal Justine."

It appeared that Captain Mason was shocked by my offer.

"But he's charged with rape, Lieutenant. You do know that, don't you?"

I agreed I knew the charge but assured the captain it made little difference to me. I had spent considerable time with

Airman Justine and felt I had good insight into his character and personality.

Captain Jud Mason agreed to use me in the court-martial. But when I showed up in his office just before the first day of the hearings were to begin, Airman Justine threw a fit.

"What's she doin' here?" he snarled in his best savage manner.

"She's willing to testify for you, Justine," the captain told him. "And I'd say you're damn lucky. It'll throw a lot of weight having a woman testify to your character in a rape case. Besides, she's an officer. That means something, too."

"No dice, Counsel. I don't want no officer sayin' nice t'ings about me."

"Don't be silly, Justine," Mason argued.

I suggested that I be allowed to talk to Justine alone. Jud Mason agreed and left us in his office.

"Airman Mal Savage Justine, I am shocked at you," I told him. "After all, I'm offering to help you. And what do you do? You turn down my help."

Justine looked at the floor and belched a few times. He cleared his throat and looked up at me.

"What was you gonna say about me?"

I gave that some thought. "I was going to say that I found you to be a kind and gentle man. I was going to say you have a true sense of respect for womanhood and that I found it inconceivable that you would violate a woman by use of force. And, most important, I was going to tell them about your being ticklish. After all, Savage, that's why you got in trouble in the first place."

The Savage leaped from his chair and screamed, "You keep your mouth shut, you hear me? I'd radda go to jail dan have people t'inkin' I was nuts or ticklish or sompin'."

He frightened me. And his outburst brought the Air Police racing into the office. Captain Jud Mason, legal counsel, was right at their heels.

The Savage yelled at Mason, "I don't want dis broad and officer sayin' not'in' fa me. It's my trial, ain't it?"

Mason took me out into the hall and talked in very confidential tones.

"Look, Lieutenant Moura, let me give you a little advice. Despite what you think, this guy Justine is bad and rotten all the way through. The best thing for the service is to see him get ten years and booted out after that. Why don't you just drop this character testimony idea, for your good and the good of the service?"

"But I can't do that, Captain," I answered. "I don't think he ever did rape that girl."

"You know what, Lieutenant? I don't think he did, either. But a guy like that probably will rape somebody someday. Let's not give him that chance."

I was dumbstruck. I looked at Captain Mason and could feel tears well up in my eyes.

"But you're supposed to defend him, Captain. Why are you talking like this?"

"Because I'm a realist. This court-martial board is all set to give it to Justine, no matter what I do. He's got a whole history of troublemaking. AWOL once. Some back talk to superior officers. Brawls. Bad debts. A bad apple. Believe me, it's best for everyone to get him out of circulation, Lieutenant."

The tears no longer welled up. They flowed over, down my cheeks and onto my uniform blouse. Captain Mason stood there, a professional look of understanding on his face.

"Airman," he called. An Air Policeman came. "I think Lieutenant Moura here wants to go back to quarters. Drive her, please."

"Yes, sir."

Chapter 26

"Two Couches—No Waiting"

"Are you going to re-up, Joni?"

"I don't know, Jackie. Are you?"

She didn't know, either. We were rapidly approaching the end of our active-duty commitment to the Air Force and were faced with the decision of whether or not to sign on for another tour of duty. The alternative was to call it quits and return to civilian nursing. Our quandary wasn't at all unique. It happens to everyone at some point in their military life.

Naturally, every branch of the Armed Forces wants its people to stay with them. After all, they've spent a great deal of time and money in training you, and a longer return on their investment is logically to be desired.

But everyone has a built-in force that rebels against staying in the Armed Forces a minute longer than absolutely necessary by law.

The internal conflict was upon us. We felt that inner tug that told us to get out of the Armed Forces. But this was at odds with the reality of our tours of duty. It had been fun. The travel was interesting and enjoyable, the people diverse and pleasant, and the challenge far greater than called for in civilian nursing. Based on all these realizations, we knew we should re-up. But the doubt remained.

We decided to talk things over with our boss of the moment, a woman major who'd proved herself to be an understanding and agreeable commanding officer. We told her of our dilemma, and she spent a great deal of time discussing the pros and cons of the military life as a career.

At the end of our session with her, she took off her glasses, reached for the phone, and dialed. While waiting for the sergeant who answered to get the person with whom the major wanted to speak, she told us whom she was calling.

"I think you ought to talk with Captain Quixot. He's a psychologist and a good one. This modern Air Force of ours believes in keeping only those people who are properly motivated and adjusted to the service. When I have people like yourselves who have doubts about staying in, I like to send them to Captain Quixot. He's able to draw them out and . . . Captain Quixot? This is Major Barnum."

The major made the appointment for the following afternoon at four. We arrived on time and were greeted by a staff sergeant.

"The captain will be with you in a minute," he said.

"Thank you."

We sat in the outer office and browsed through some of the magazines. There were some on mental health, a few copies of *True Confessions*, a single issue of *Evergreen*, and a whole stack of *Jack and Jill*. I was in the middle of a gripping fairy tale when the sergeant asked us into the captain's office.

We were both slightly taken aback by the initial introduction to Captain Quixot. He was a little man with funny little half-glasses and a curl of hair sticking straight up from the middle of a bald dome. And he was obviously very nervous. His eyes shifted back and forth, and his hand was limp and sweaty when we shook it.

"Sit down, please," he said, pointing to the floor.

"Here?"

"No, no, no. I'll get some chairs." He went into the outer office and dragged two chairs into his office. We reached to help, but he shook his head and struggled with them himself.

We sat in the chairs, and Captain Quixot leaned on his desk, a fretful look on his face. He started biting his nails and chewing the inside of his cheek. Finally he sat in his chair and looked right past us toward the door.

"Will you stay in the Air Force?" he asked weakly.

"We don't know, sir," Jackie answered. "Major Barnum thought we should talk to you about it."

"Yes. I suppose that's a good idea." His eyes were still on the door. "Yes. We'll talk about that."

There was silence. Captain Quixot shifted his gaze to the telephone. He looked at it a long time, and it rang.

"I'll get it, I'll get it," he yelled to the sergeant. "Hello? Oh, hello, Richard. . . . But we don't want to go with them . . . we have our own club. Besides, the last time we went with them some of them brought along whiskey and ruined everything. . . . All right, Richard. Whatever you think."

Quixot hung up and bit his nails again. Then a small spark seemed to light in his eyes, and he looked directly at us for the first time.

"Do you like birds?" he asked.

We nodded that we did.

"But I've never seen you at the club."

"What club?"

"The base bird-watching club. I'm vice-president."

"Hey, that's marvelous. Congratulations."

"Oh, it's not so wonderful. Hard work and dedication brought me to the position. I'm surprised you haven't attended any of our meetings and watches."

"Well, sir, we like birds but not *that* much."

"I know, I know. Too many people feel that way. But I'll

bet that if you came a few times you'd learn to love them just as we do. Why, I remember when Sergeant Hackum first came. He's one of the base chefs, you know. He knew all about birds and their anatomical structure, but he couldn't even tell the difference between an eagle and a tiny little sparrow." He snickered. "But pretty soon he learned all about the birds, and now he's one of our most expert watchers in the club."

"That's marvelous," I offered through clenched teeth.

"Yes, it is. Now, you must come to one of our meetings. The next one. That's Monday night. My wife is secretary, and she'll be there, too."

"We'll try, sir."

"I know you will. And I'll make you a bet right now ... for a soda ... that once you get involved in the club, you'll decide to stay in the Air Force."

"We wanted to talk to you about that, sir. You see, we were speaking with Major Barnum about it, and she suggested ..."

"I know. I know. But let me ask you one simple and basic question. Answer this and you'll be able to answer the big question."

We waited for the question, but it never came.

We waited some more.

"What question was that, sir?"

He was biting his nails, and his face had a pained expression on it.

"The question, sir."

Captain Quixot leaned across the desk, his chin in his hands, and said, "You wouldn't really go out there, would you?"

"Out where?"

"Civilian life."

"Why not, sir?"

He shook his head and pursed his lips.

"The world is falling down. It's much more secure here."

"Oh."

"You go out there and compete and fight and chase the golden rainbow and it destroys you. Don't you agree?"

"Well, sir, it didn't seem so bad to us. But we have loved being in the Air Force, and we're just a little confused about what to do next."

"Yes, I know. I was confused, too. But think about all those high doctor and dental bills you'll have to pay. Think about the price of food in our inflation period. Think of

286

never really knowing who you work for and buttering up all those people. Think of ... think of ... think of having to decide every day what to wear."

"You have a point there, sir. And thank you very much." We arose in unison and headed for the door.

"But what about the meeting?"

"We'll be there."

"Oh, that's good. When you see all the advantages available in the Air Force, you'll find that decision you're faced with much easier to make. Eight o'clock. In the mess hall."

"Yes, sir. 'Bye."

Captain Quixot was a nice man, we decided. A little timid perhaps, but nice. We didn't attend his bird watcher's meeting and we didn't re-up. Our decision had nothing to do with Captain Quixot. It probably had more to do with that inner force that dictates decisions in such matters. Historically, the military service has been a necessary but brief detour in almost everyone's life cycle. To consider pursuing it beyond the required length of duty brings out all sorts of negative reactions from friends, family, and perfect strangers. It's really a shame because, viewed without bias, the military life can be rewarding and fun for many individuals. It was for us. And obviously it was for Captain Quixot.

There are many times we wish we were back in the Air Force. But, as the saying goes, everybody's got to be someplace, and we're here—working as nurses, being females and coincidentally authors of the book you've just read and, we hope, enjoyed.

We should mention that the names have been changed to protect all the guilty parties. Anyone is free to use anything they wish from this book provided they are willing to pay handsomely for the right. And if anyone can find political motivations between the covers of this book, he or she is simply looking too hard. As Ginger Whip once said, "I used to be engaged to a politician."

We'll leave it at that.

"At ease!"

FAWCETT CREST BOOKS
ON TOP WITH THE BESTSELLERS

IN THIS HOUSE OF BREDE		
Rumer Godden	P1466	$1.25
THE FAME GAME Rona Jaffe	M1477	95¢
TH KING'S PLEASURE Norah Lofts	M1478	95¢
THE LOST QUEEN Norah Lofts	M1398	95¢
THE PARABLES OF PEANUTS		
Robert L. Short	M1479	95¢
THE PROMISE Chaim Potok	P1449	$1.25
MR. BRIDGE Evan S. Connell, Jr.	M1451	95¢
MRS. BRIDGE Evan S. Connell, Jr.	M1452	95¢
THE DAY OF THE DOLPHIN		
Robert Merle	M1438	95¢
COP! L. H. Whittemore	M1439	95¢
THE DEATH COMMITTEE		
Noah Gordon	M1444	95¢
SILENT SPRING Rachel Carson	M1455	95¢
ADA Vladimir Nabokov	P1409	$1.25
THE GODFATHER Mario Puzo	Q1388	$1.50
THEM Joyce Carol Oates	P1467	$1.25
EXPENSIVE PEOPLE Joyce Carol Oates	M1408	95¢
LADY OF MALLOW Dorothy Eden	T1470	75¢
SIEGE IN THE SUN Dorothy Eden	M1450	95¢
THE VINES OF YARRABEE		
Dorothy Eden	M1365	95¢

FAWCETT WORLD LIBRARY
WHEREVER PAPERBACKS ARE SOLD